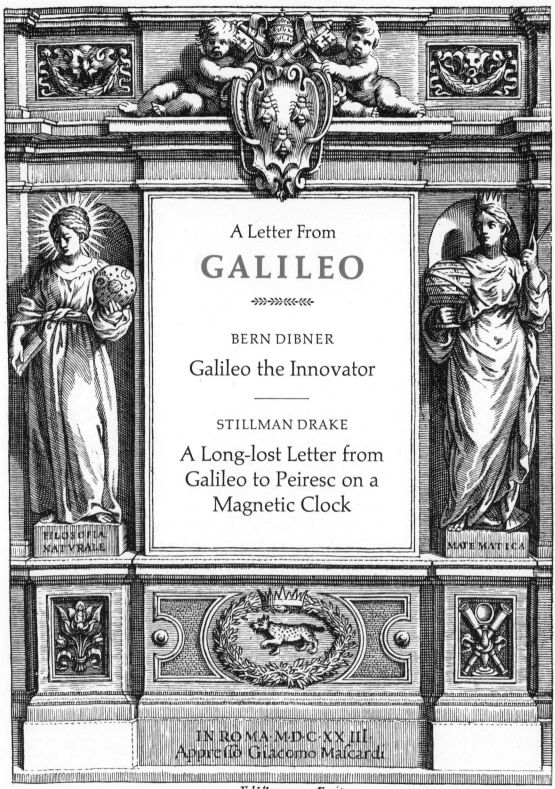

A Letter From

GALILEO

➤➤➤➤➤►◄◄◄◄◄

BERN DIBNER

Galileo the Innovator

———

STILLMAN DRAKE

A Long-lost Letter from
Galileo to Peiresc on a
Magnetic Clock

FILOSOFIA
NATVRALE

MATEMATICA

IN ROMA·M·D·C·XXIII·
Appreſſo Giacomo Maſcardi

F·Villamoena Fecit·

BURNDY LIBRARY · NORWALK, CONNECTICUT · 1967

"In the same way a man will never become a philosopher by worrying forever about the writings of other men, without ever raising his own eyes to nature's works in the attempt to recognize there the truths already known and to investigate some of the infinite number that remain to be discovered."

—Galileo, Note on J. C. Lagalla,
De Phaenominis in Orbe Lunae, 1612.

PUBLICATION NO. 24

The frame used on the title page is from Galileo, Il Saggiatore, *1623. All of the illustrations used in this publication are from sources in the Burndy Library, except as indicated.*

To

Dottoressa MARIA LUISA BONELLI

*Valiant guardian of the legacy of Tuscany
in the natural and physical sciences*

GALILEO GALILEI

His innovations in astronomy, physics and mechanics helped usher in the modern world of science. He advanced celestial discoveries and stirred conflicts with conservative teachers and theologians who retarded the progress that he fostered. His long-lost letter here discussed helps shed light on events following his trial, and on his design for a magnetic clock.

A LETTER FROM GALILEO

GALILEO the INNOVATOR

by Bern Dibner

BY the mere chance of time, place and profession, Galileo Galilei became a figure of profound significance in history. Instinct drew his scholarly interests into a concern with science and a reliance on measurement and instrumentation. A keen analytic mind buttressed by a strong will and an impatience with conformity and traditionalism made this Tuscan the figure that opened the door thru which history moved from medievalism into modern times. He has been considered the most influential scientist since Aristotle.* The qualities that caused Galileo to understand and accept the Copernican approach were also those that prompted him to struggle against the restrictions in scientific investigation by church and governmental authority. In today's comparative freedom of intellectual and scientific inquiry, Galileo has become a symbol of the passage over the threshold from speculation into scientific inquiry.

Galileo was born in Pisa on 15 February 1564 (the same year as Shakespeare). Pisa lies, like Florence, on the Arno River, but near the Mediterranean over which her ships at one time were dominant. She lost her proud independence to Florence in 1509 but her fine public buildings and the university, founded in 1338, made this ancient city one of the most important cultural centers in Italy. The ravages of two severe wars against Genoa and Florence had sapped the manhood of Pisa from which she never recovered her greatness. At the time of Galileo's birth the population of Pisa had been reduced to less than 10,000.

The Galilei had once been a prominent noble Florentine family of which 19 members had served their city in the Signoria. Galileo's father, Vincenzio, was a man of talent for the arts rather than for the accumulation of wealth. He was a competent musician who wrote on music and mathematics. In spite of slender means, young Galileo was encouraged in his studies and was sent to the local school.

The time of Galileo's youth was most exciting, especially in Tuscany. America had been discovered and the significance of the circumnavigation of the earth was profound to all the thinking people of the time. Ships from the Mediterranean had also penetrated the ports of Africa, India, the East Indies and China. New herbs, plants, people and animals were discovered and studied. By these fresh explorations and new discoveries, doubt was cast on the knowledge and authority formerly contained in the ancient and classic writings. The new anatomy of Vesalius cast doubt on older medical views, and the new cosmos of Copernicus was being discussed among

*WHITE, Jr., Lynn, "Pumps and Pendula: Galileo and Technology" in *Galileo Reappraised*, U.C.L.A., 1966.

scholars. Above it all hung the heavy cloud of religious uncertainty because the winds of the Reformation were blowing southward.

The lessons in Latin and Greek that Galileo acquired at the school of a local master were supplemented by instruction at home from his learned father. At about 13 years of age Galileo moved to a Benedictine monastery at Vallombrosa where instruction in the classic languages and logic helped to shape his future interest.

As the oldest of a family of seven with a proud but ailing and impoverished father, Galileo growing into young manhood had practical considerations in mind in the choice of a career. At 17, in 1581, he matriculated as a student of medicine at the University of Pisa. There his constant questioning of the text and lectures held before him made him stand out as an unusual individualist. It also made him unpopular with the more conservative teachers and fellow students. Astronomy was then included in the medical course because the occult influence of the heavens was still accepted as influencing the health as well as the fortune of individuals.

The year of matriculation at the university was the same year in which he observed the isochronous oscillation of a bronze lamp hanging from the high roof of the nave of the Cathedral of Pisa. When the church attendant drew the lamp toward him, lit it and released it to swing in its arc, young Galileo, using his pulse for timing, observed that the oscillations remained in the same period of time, irrespective of the length of the arc. This, then, brings us into the first of three areas of special interest in the present study—chronometrics. Galileo

discovered the law of the pendulum and that was to lead to the development of the practical clock. He was also concerned with magnetism, a new force in which Galileo showed considerable interest, especially in his concept of a magnetic clock. Finally, he wrote of his continued difficulties with the Church, a long and involved chapter in the history of enlightenment under which Galileo was still smarting when he penned the subject letter in 1635.

Relating the oscillation of the pendulum to the beat of his pulse led Galileo to a suggestion of three types of pendula with which to measure the rate of one's pulse beat. In principle all had a pendulum of varying lengths by which the pendulum bob might be raised or lowered until the beat corresponded to the rate of the pulse. The indication of the pendulum length could then be read on any of the scales and the beat assessed as languid or lively. He called the devices "pulsilogia". A half century later, Galileo was to return to the pendulum principle in his design for an astronomical clock.

At the University of Pisa

Galileo became more attracted to mathematics than to medicine by listening to the lectures of a Florentine friend of the family, a mathematician named Ostilio Ricci. Slowly Euclid replaced Hippocrates as a prime interest of the young student, and the fact that a professor of mathematics then earned a tenth or a hundredth part of the salary of a professor of medicine, theology or law meant little to Galileo. This shift of interest did not help in his required final studies; therefore, after nearly four years at the University of Pisa, Galileo withdrew without the grant of a doctor's degree. Released from formal classes, he plunged into physics and mathematics, especially studying the works of Archimedes, whose tradition he was to continue into modern times.

From these studies in physics came a series of new concepts and scientific ideas. In 1586 he described his hydrostatic balance by the means of which one could determine the relative components in an alloy of two metals. This led him to an intensive study of the center of gravity of solids, the results of which were circulated in manuscript copies but which were first printed in 1638. We thus see the classic investigations of Archimedes, quiescent for nearly two millennia, finally extended. Galileo's reputation spread and he attracted friends who saw quality in his fresh approach. Among these was the distinguished mathematician, the Marquis Guidobaldo del Monte of Pesaro, who stood by him in later times of trouble.

In spite of the recognition being accorded Galileo, his meager income was no great help to his father's family. He therefore sought a professorship in any of several universities where a position in mathematics or some similar discipline was open. He tried Bologna without results. Later he tried Padua but was equally unsuccessful. He inquired at Pisa but met political as well as academic obstacles. During the two years 1587 to 1589 Galileo tutored students while waiting for an appointment. When, as mid-1589 approached, the chair in mathematics in Pisa was again open, Galileo applied and was accepted. The salary was pitifully small but Galileo was now 25 and could not be a chooser. His professional career had begun.

In his new post he faced the clutter of staid Aristotelian science, the soundness of which Galileo had already begun to question. He approached the problems with a double stride—the one of logic, the other of experiment. One he used to arrive at an opinion, the other to demonstrate and prove its verity. Having once dedicated himself to checking some of Aristotle's contentions, Galileo was not one to keep to himself any contradictions that he discovered. But such iconoclasms were quickly taken up by the students, and the young professor's brash statements irritated and disturbed his more mature colleagues, the churchmen and the establishment that had had enough of recent questioning of authority.

It was at about this time that Galileo was supposed to have demonstrated the fallacy of the assertion by Aristotle that if two different weights of the same substance were dropped from a high point, the heavier body would reach the ground correspondingly faster than the lighter one. The disproving of this contention by Galileo in actually letting two such weights fall from the Leaning Tower of Pisa is as traditional as the story of the swinging cathedral lamp, and both* are deeply woven into the fabric of the legends of science.

Many years later, speaking in the name of Salviati (one of the participants in his *Dialog Concerning the Two Principal Systems of the World*) Galileo stated ". . . a ball of one, ten, a hundred, or a thousand pounds will all measure the same hundred yards in the same time."** Since the Tower

---

* The one is treated in COOPER, L., *Aristotle, Galileo and the Tower of Pisa*, Cornell, 1935; the other in TAYLOR, F. S., *Galileo and the Freedom of Thought*, London, 1938.
** DRAKE, *Dialogue*, p. 238. See footnote on page 21.

of Pisa is about one hundred "yards" (braccia, of approximately 21 to 22 inches each) in height, the basis for the legend of the famous experiment has some confirmation. An object would fall from the Tower's top (179 feet) in somewhat more than three seconds, making timing without a stopwatch not feasible at that time. Only relative timing could have been tried but the gross error of Aristotle would be demonstrated.*

Such scoffing at established notions held for two thousand years was not taken lightly by Galileo's elder colleagues at Pisa. Animosities became apparent and Galileo was subjected to petty annoyances, some of of which came from high political positions. When his three-year term expired he felt he was not welcome at Pisa. He therefore resigned and sought a teaching post in Florence. He soon felt the lack of position and income especially keenly because his father had died a year before (July 1591), and the family responsibility weighed now more heavily upon him.

To the University of Padua

With help from his friend the Marquis Guidobaldo, Galileo in 1592 accepted the professorship in mathematics at the famous University of Padua, founded in 1238. Not only was this university better established in the sciences, but the salary was considerably higher than at Pisa and the appointment was for four years plus a probable

* Galileo's work in determining the value of acceleration due to gravity has been honored by the establishment of standard unit of acceleration called the *gal*. It is an acceleration of one centimeter per second each second; it has assumed rising importance in the jet and space age.

renewal for two years more. Unlike the atmosphere of learning in Tuscany, strongly dominated by a corrupt nobility and a powerful church, Galileo found the conditions in Padua, part of the Republic of Venice, those of comparative freedom of thought and expression. The independent Venetians whose trade over a wide area brought an expanded point of view encouraged individual opinion.

In such an atmosphere, the innate abilities of Galileo responded in a stream of innovations in mathematics, astronomy, dynamics, mechanics and military science. He prepared treatises which he distributed in manuscript among his pupils and forwarded a few to colleagues in other cities. In his first letter to Kepler in which he thanked the author for sending him a new and important book, he was profuse in his appreciation and expressed concern over the limitations placed by authority on scientific disclosure. In the letter dated 4 August 1597, Galileo also said, "This I shall do the more willingly because many years ago I became a convert to the opinions of Copernicus, and by his theory have succeeded in explaining many phenomena which on the contrary hypothesis are altogether inexplicable. I have arranged many arguments and confutations of the opposite opinions, which however, I have not yet dared to publish, fearing the fate of our master, Copernicus, who, although he has earned immortal fame among a few, yet by an infinite number (for so only can the number of fools be measured) is hissed and derided."* The correspondence between the two

* Quoted in FAHIE, J. J., *Galileo, His Life and Work*, London, 1903, p. 40.

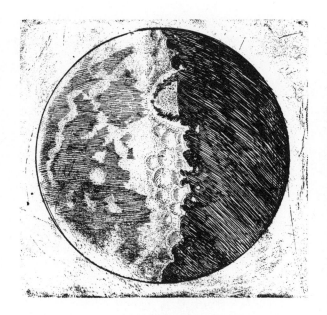

Galileo, *Siderius Nuncius*, 1610

The smooth and "perfect" moon surface of Aristotle was shown to be mountainous and pitted in Galileo's telescope. Seen also were the satellites of Jupiter, the innumerable stars of the Milky Way and the galaxies of Orion and the Pleiades.

astronomers continued and was ended only by the death of Kepler in 1630.

The first general public notice of this mathematics professor who had demonstrated an interest in practical ways and instrumentation was his invention of what he termed his Geometrical and Military Compass, later known as a Sector or Proportional Divider. This instrument found considerable use in architecture, surveying and ballistics and he claimed to have sold thousands of them. The orders for such compasses came to Galileo from many European countries and prompted him to set up an instrument shop for making and selling them and other scientific instruments, including drawing instruments and magnetic compasses. The description and use of this compass formed the substance of his first printed book*; it appeared in Padua in July 1606 from a press set up in Galileo's own house and is one of the rarest books in the history of science.

As confidence in his ability and his reputation became firm, the period of his appointment of six years ended in October 1599. The stay was therefore renewed for another six years and at an increase in salary of almost double his former pay. His reputation attracted students from many parts of Europe, among them young nobles and student scientists who were later to be prominent in history.

Another device that Galileo invented in this term (1602) was an air thermometer. In its early form this indicating device was essentially a reservoir of water the size of an egg. Into it was set a narrow glass tube

---

* *Le Operazioni del Compasso Geometrico et Militari di Galileo Galilei.*

the top of which terminated in a bulb from which the air had been partially exhausted. The water column rose and fell in the tube with changes in temperature.*

Galileo's understanding and interpretation of the physics of Aristotle occupied the first phase of his scientific studies and writing. He then moved into astronomy with results that fundamentally changed that ancient science.

The New Astronomy

Galileo's abiding interest in astronomy was sharpened at Padua in 1604 with the appearance on 10 October of a brilliant new star in the constellation of the Serpent. It was the brightest star in the sky with only the exception of Venus. At a time when the health and fortunes of men were considered closely bound to signs in the heavens, the new star aroused great popular interest and astronomers were questioned about its significance. That there should be any change in the immutable pattern of the heavens (other than a "sub-lunar" comet) went counter to the teachings of Aristotle, and Galileo's disbelief mounted as the new star continued in brilliance and remained in its position among the other "fixed" stars.

The significance of this new body in the heavens was its challenge to the Aristotelian concept of an unchanging, orderly heaven where all was perfect and nothing could be new. The very presence of the new star (or nova) raised questions among the

more alert students and controversy arose wherever they gathered. Galileo boldly presented his view and explanation based on the system of Copernicus, repudiating the ancient teachings of Aristotle and Ptolemy (which he himself had earlier taught). The new star showed no parallax and remained in the heavens for 18 months, a tantalizingly long period for both Galileo and his adversaries, yet short enough to demonstrate celestial change.

The geocentric system of Aristotle was one in which the spherical earth was at rest while the moon, sun and five planets moved within the sphere of the fixed stars that rotated daily about the earth. To this general system Ptolemy, in about 140 A.D., provided mathematical support in his book called the *Almagest**; the system remained the authoritative one until questioned by Copernicus in 1543. The momentum of the Ptolemaic system gave it acceptance for centuries after Copernicus but the logic and mathematics of Galileo, backed by his new instrument, the telescope, helped to force the change. Kepler's convincing laws of orbital motion and Newton's exposition of universal gravitation clearly fitted in with the new astronomy and led to our modern adventures in space rocketry and the advances in satellite engineering. Copernicus had stopped the revolving celestial sphere and Bruno saw limitless cosmic space beyond the stars. Galileo moved toward these views.

An event of greatest importance in the

---

* About ten years later Galileo substituted alcohol for water. His former pupil Duke Ferdinando II colored the alcohol and reduced the tube diameter. Francesco Lana in 1670 substituted mercury for water. Fahrenheit introduced his scale in 1724; the Réaumur scale appeared in 1730, and Celsius proposed the Centigrade scale in 1742.

---

* CLAUDIUS PTOLEMY (A.D. 90–168) of Alexandria wrote this book in Greek; it was translated into Arabic in 827, its name signifying "greatest of all books". It went thru many translations and editions, first being printed from a fresh translation by Regiomontanus in Venice, 1496.

life of Galileo and in astronomy occurred in June 1609 when, as he later wrote in his *Siderius Nuncius*, "Ten months ago, barely, a rumor came to our ears that an optical instrument had been elaborated by a Dutchman, by the aid of which visible objects, even though far distant from the eye of the observer, were distinctly seen as if near at hand; and some stories of their marvelous effect were bandied about, to which some gave credence and which others denied. . . . I first prepared a tube of lead, in the ends of which I fitted two glass lenses, both plane on one side, one being spherically convex, the other concave, on the other side."

The first telescope made by Galileo was probably completed in July 1609 and in August he wrote to the Doge of Venice offering him a telescope as a gift. Shortly thereafter Galileo demonstrated the telescope to the Doge and to the Venetian Senate. The practical promise of such an instrument to a seafaring people was very welcome and the authorities responded by a substantial increase in Galileo's salary. The demonstration was followed by requests for many such instruments which Galileo found difficult to fabricate. Improvements in the making of his telescopes soon raised the magnification from three to about 10 power, then to 30 power.

In January 1610 the telescope was turned toward the sky and the first of a series of major astronomical discoveries began. Galileo saw that the surface of the moon was not smooth but was marked by ridges, mountains (which he correctly estimated as about four miles in height) and craters as well as "seas". During 7-13 January he discovered that the planet Jupiter had four satellites moving near it and he proceeded to plot their motion on succeeding nights. They moved close to the ecliptic and were evidently revolving around the planet. The significance of this hitherto unobserved fact was that there existed motion of heavenly bodies in closed paths around another planet and not around the earth as the center. The changing phases of Venus discovered late in 1610 seemed also to describe motion around the sun.

He observed the countless stars of the Milky Way, the vastly greater number of stars than had ever been expected, the phases of the moon—in all, nine major discoveries. With this instrument more of the new in the heavens had been exposed to Galileo than had to any previous astronomer. Many of these were announced in his *Siderius Nuncius**, one of the most important heralds of science. Engravings and other illustrations of the moon brought the first indications to the earthbound reader of what the earth's satellite was really like. He referred to the planets of Jupiter as "never seen from the first beginning of the world until our time".

With such disturbing information, Galileo felt more strongly than ever that a revision of celestial patterns was to be brought about, that a new world had opened up before him and that he was to be its interpreter. He wrote, "Here we have a fine and elegant argument for quieting the doubts of those who, while accepting with tranquil mind the revolutions of the planets about the sun in the Copernican system, are mightily disturbed to have the moon alone revolve about the earth and accompany it in an annual rotation about the sun. Some

---

* GALILEO, *Siderius Nuncius*, Venetiis, 1610, p. 28.

have believed that this structure of the universe should be rejected as impossible. But now we have not just one planet rotating about another while both run through a great orbit around the sun; our own eyes show us four stars which wander around Jupiter as does the moon around the earth, while all together trace out a grand revolution about the sun in the space of twelve years."*

He also first observed the rings of Saturn but the limited magnifying power of his telescope** prevented a clear image. Nearly five decades had to pass before Huygens clearly saw and described them. The riddle of Saturn was followed by the observation that Venus had phases similar to those of the moon. He counted 40 fixed stars in the constellation Pleiades as against only six to be seen with the naked eye. "I have also observed a multitude of fixed stars that had never been seen before which are more than ten times as numerous as those which are visible to the naked eye."

Involved as Galileo was in 1609 and 1610 with his work with the telescope and the cornucopia of celestial discoveries, he derived little from the large tome that Kepler had just sent him. The *Astronomia Nova*

disclosed the first two of Kepler's laws of celestial motion—planets moved about the sun in elliptical orbits; they covered equal areas in equal times. Ten years later the third law—the planets' period of motion—also reached Galileo and was equally disregarded. Galileo was then struggling with the concept of inertia and for once mathematical considerations became subordinate to the order and harmony of circular orbital motion. Kepler's suggestion that some magnetic force shaped the orbits was also for him without conviction.

The last of the great discoveries in this series was observed in 1611 and then published in March 1613.* It described sun spots which he interpreted as clouds of vaporizable material on the sun's surface that rotated with the sun. The changeless heavens of Aristotle thus suffered additional doubts.

While some freer minds among Galileo's colleagues caught the spirit of the innovations, change came slowly in those days and there were many dissenters, doubters and strong antagonists. Some interpreted Galileo's observations as a hoax, as optical illusions, as rays refracted by Galileo's instrument, as impossible and therefore unobservable. Some refused to look thru the telescope; one such, an instructor at Pisa named Libri, refused to look. Later, after Libri had died, Galileo wrote, "Libri did not choose to see my celestial trifles while he was on earth; perhaps he will do so, now that he has gone to heaven." Galileo gained considerable comfort from the confirmation of his discoveries by the Jesuit astrono-

---

* This small quarto was printed in Venice, 1610 and consists of only 30 leaves. Its title has been translated as *The Heavenly Message*. Kepler was so impressed by the contents of Galileo's book that he published two works in its support. When the original edition of 550 copies was sold out, a reissue appeared in Frankfurt in the same year as the original publication. The rapidity of the spread of the discovery in Galileo's small book is shown by the appearance of these discoveries in Chinese in Peking, only five years after its initial appearance, issued by a Jesuit missionary there.

** The resolving power of Galileo's telescope was about nine fold or three seconds of arc, enough to observe the satellites of Jupiter; the resolving power of the unaided eye is about one minute of arc.

---

* *Istoria e Dimostrazioni intorno alle Macchie Solari*, Roma, 1613.

mer and chief mathematician at the Collegio Romano, Christopher Clavius, who had earlier rejected these discoveries. Illness prevented Galileo's visit to Rome in 1610 but Father Clavius was his host when Galileo came to Rome in the following year.

Return to Tuscany

With the rise of his reputation as an excellent mathematician and astronomer, offers came to Galileo from other princes and distant universities. A very attractive offer came from Tuscany where Grand Duke Cosimo II proffered Galileo the post of First and Extraordinary Mathematician at his old University of Pisa and the Duke's First Philosopher and Mathematician. The salary was high and he was to have few duties other than an occasional lecture to a limited number of the nobility. Galileo hesitated leaving the free atmosphere of Venice where the Church influence of Rome was minimal. However, the temptation of salary, position, a nostalgia for Tuscany and closeness to the Grand Duke outweighed other considerations and Galileo left Venice for Florence.

Welcome as such a short-range change was to the material welfare of Galileo and his family, the pressures of the old-school philosophers and conservative churchmen soon began to be felt. Tracts and pamphlets appeared criticizing the new astronomy, finding it contrary to Scripture, repeating the Joshua story, also that of the shot fired vertically upward or the weight dropped from the top of the mast. In the controversy it was the word of an innovator and his new telescope versus the authority of "common

sense", timeless tradition and the right people.

Galileo made a journey to Rome in March 1611 where he was well received by high churchmen and by scholars. He was honored by his scientific colleagues and elected as the sixth member of the Accademia dei Lincei, an outstanding body of philosophers. Yet between 1610 and 1616 the heat of controversy was whipped up by his or-

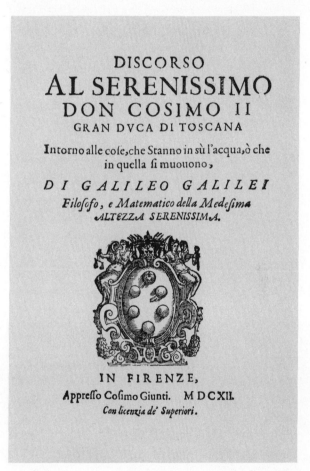

In 1612 Galileo published his book on the physics of floating bodies containing his earliest discoveries. This copy has been shown by Stillman Drake to have autograph corrections in Galileo's hand.

thodox opponents, especially those among the Dominicans.

Grand Duke Cosimo often invited dignitaries and scholars to his palace for dinner and encouraged discussions of current topics. Present at one such dinner in September 1611 was Galileo who led a discussion on floating bodies, especially discoursing on why ice floated. Supporting his views was Cardinal Maffeo Barberini who later as Pope Urban VIII was to play such a stirring role in Galileo's future. Another cardinal, Ferdinand Gonzaga, sided with Galileo's opponents. It was the suggestion of the Grand Duke to shape the arguments into a published work; it appeared in Florence in 1612 as a *Discourse on Floating Bodies*. Written in Italian, it first marshalled the traditional but incorrect arguments; Galileo then proceeded to reduce them by fact and experiment to absurdities.

The discussion of the existence or non-existence of new satellites and moon mountains reached into the highest places. Friends asked Galileo questions about them and he often replied in writing. One such presentation of his position was a letter to the Grand Duchess Christina di Lorena*, written 21 December 1613. Galileo attempted to take the astronomical science out of the realm of theology but he was a layman and, altho a devout Catholic, was treading on territory reserved for theologians. The Church had already suffered too much of this kind of invasion that was held to have led to the Reformation. It was another manifestation at the beginning of the

insurgent century. As Stillman Drake has it, "Ostensibly this battle was waged over the Copernican system; in reality it was fought over the right of a scientist to teach and defend his scientific beliefs. The real issue was perfectly clear to Galileo at all times, as it was to some of the theologians who were soon to decide the contest against him. But by his avowed enemies in the Church it seems never to have been understood at all. To their minds Galileo was attacking the Church; to his own mind he was protecting it from the commission of a fatal error."* This led to his letter to the Grand Duchess.

Beginning in 1613 the hunt for cosmological heresy took on the fervor of a mission, and two Dominicans, Father Caccini and Father Lorini, were loudest in their denunciation of the new liberties being taken by astronomers and mathematicians. Father Lorini "transcribed" a letter that Galileo had sent to his pupil, the Dominican Father Castelli, but altered the sense of important passages before sending it on to the Inquisition via Cardinal Sfondrati in February 1615. While the secret sessions were being held, Galileo, unaware of them, thought it wise to keep his friends in Rome advised; he therefore sent an authentic copy of his *Letter to Castelli* to Monsignor Dini asking that it be shown to the Jesuit mathematicians and possibly to Cardinal Bellarmin, or even to the Pope. Further, Galileo indicated that now was the time for the Church to recognize the validity of the Copernican view as a physical reality and not in conflict with Holy Writ.

Before the year was over, and again in

---

*Christina of Lorraine, mother of Grand Duke Cosimo II. The letter was circulated in manuscript and was first printed in Italian and Latin in Strasbourg in 1636 in a very small edition; it was suppressed in Catholic countries.

*DRAKE, Stillman, *Discoveries and Opinions of Galileo*, New York, 1957, p. 145.

Florence, open warfare on the Copernican doctrine was preached by churchmen. Action against Galileo broke on 5 February 1615 when the Dominican monk, Lorini, denounced Galileo's letter* to Castelli before the Holy Office. The letter was found to have five minor errors of doctrine when the matter was brought before the Inquisition. The case fell thru and Galileo was absolved. The irritation persisted and further investigations went on during 1615. Later, another churchman, Father Ximenes, denounced Galileo's book on sunspots before the Inquisition in Florence. In February 1616, a special commission appointed by the Pope delivered its censure against any proposals that the sun is the center of the world, that the earth is not its center or that it moves in a diurnal motion. Just as the church fathers had warned Galileo not to become involved in matters of theology, so they permitted themselves the blunder of judging matters of natural science. Such involvement both St. Augustine and Galileo had warned them not to attempt. In his letter to the Grand Duchess, Galileo tried passionately to prevent his church from committing the error of declaring the Copernican doctrine as heretical. His bias even led to some exaggerations** in his appeal for an open mind in understanding heliocentrism.

The culmination of the official action against Galileo was the summoning of the astronomer by Cardinal Bellarmin to his palace, an injunction to the extent and substance of his teaching of Copernicanism and the issuance of a decree on 25 February 1616 by the Holy Office acting on the opinion of the Assessor and a group of theologians. It declared ". . . that the Pythagorean doctrine—which is false and altogether opposed to the Holy Scripture—of the motion of the Earth, and the immobility of the Sun, which is also taught by Nicolaus Copernicus. . . ." In substance, Galileo was enjoined, in the presence of Bellarmin, ". . . to relinquish altogether the said opinion that the Sun is the center of the world and immovable and that the Earth moves; nor further to hold, teach, or defend it in any way whatsoever, verbally or in writing; otherwise proceedings would be taken against him by the Holy Office." The original injunction is missing from the otherwise orderly files of the Vatican and the substitution of an unsigned and unwitnessed administrative memorandum has been the subject of much study by scholars of the past century.*

Galileo's acquiescence to the injunction was followed by a papal audience granted to Galileo on 11 March that lasted nearly an hour. Later came the issuance of a certificate given on 26 May by Bellarmin stating ". . . that the said Signor Galileo has not abjured, either in our hand, or the hand of any other person here in Rome, or anywhere else, so far as we know, any opinion or doctrine held by him; neither has any salutary penance been imposed on him; but that only the declaration made by the Holy Father and published by the Sacred Congregation of the Index has been notified to him, wherein it is set forth that the doctrine attributed to Copernicus, that the Earth moves around the Sun and that the Sun is

*This letter has been modified to become Galileo's letter to the Grand Duchess Christina.
**ROSEN, Edward, *Galileo's Misstatements about Copernicus*, M.I.T. Press, 1958.

*de SANTILLANA, Giorgio, *The Crime of Galileo*, Chicago, 1955, Chapter VI, pp. 123, 126, 132.

stationary in the center of the world and does not move from east to west, is contrary to the Holy Scriptures and therefore cannot be defended or held." This was intended to stop the gossip hinting that Galileo had indeed been severely reprimanded and enjoined in his teaching.

A further result was that on 5 March 1616* the *De revolutionibus* of Copernicus was placed on the Index of Prohibited Books. In the years that followed Galileo was to find himself in conflict with the several interpretations of the edict of the Inquisition but the certificate given to Galileo by Cardinal Bellarmin was felt to be a partial vindication and that the astronomer could feel free to discuss and teach the new doctrine as long as he published nothing defending it. However, the passage of time proved that discussion was discouraged, publication throttled and investigation threatened. Galileo shrank into silence, but he warned that "These are the innovations which are bound to lead to the ruin of states and to the subversion of commonwealths," as he noted in his copy of his most famous book.

Following his confrontation with the church, Galileo was now at the height of his intellectual powers, enjoying considerable freedom from teaching duties, receiving a good income and access to books of reference. He was however constrained to publish and for seven years nothing by him appeared in print. He personally missed the excitement of controversy and the challenge of argument. During this time he

maintained negotiations with Spanish authorities on the possible sale of a method of determining longitude by the use of his telescope and a table of the daily position of the satellites of Jupiter.

The lifetime of Galileo being also that of the greatest activity in navigation and exploration, the solving of the problem of position in latitude and longitude became of utmost importance. With the use of the astrolabe and other instruments, one's latitude could be fairly well determined. Longitude, on the other hand, remained an unsolved problem without even theoretical assistance until two fundamental contributions were offered by Galileo. The first was the observation of the position of the satellites of Jupiter thru his telescope. These provided simultaneous observations of a celestial event at various points on the earth's surface and, thereby, the time difference between such observation and local time could be converted into a difference in longitude. The second was the application of isochronism of the pendulum which later evolved into the pendulum clock and finally into the marine chronometer.*

Two papers, one presenting Galileo's theory of the tides and the second on the nature of comets (both basically in error), were now circulated and added no great credit to him. They indicate his reaction to being prohibited from engaging in his prime concern—the structure of the universe as interpreted by Copernicus. Galileo's choice of the use of tidal motion to prove the actual diurnal motion of the earth and the validity of the Copernican system was convincing neither to the Pope, the

---

*This is one of the darker years in the calendar of history for in addition to the ban on teaching of heliocentrism by Galileo and the placing of the *De revolutionibus* on the Index, it was the year in which Shakespeare and Cervantes died. This year is counted by some as the end of the Renaissance.

*WATERS, D. W., "Galileo and Longitude", PHYSIS, III, 1964.

Holy Office nor to science, but then, as de Santillana has indicated, the Foucault pendulum to demonstrate such rotation was still two centuries in the future.

Galileo sank deeper into the quagmire of controversy when, in 1623, he issued his *Il Saggiatore* (The Assayer), a work on which he spent two years. It was a reply to a polemic from a Jesuit, and concerned itself with a discourse on the relations of friction and heat in which Galileo used brilliant argument and reference to promote the experimental method of scientific determination. The book was dedicated to the newly elected Pope Urban VIII (the former Cardinal Maffeo Barberini), who was very favorably disposed to Galileo.

The election in August 1623 of Cardinal Barberini as Pope Urban VIII restored courage to the heart of Galileo. In spite of his indifferent health, he broke out of his retirement of eight years of imposed seclusion and, in April 1624, Galileo arrived in Rome to visit his old friend, now the Pope. Galileo soon found that with Europe torn by the religious Thirty Years War, Urban was more concerned with matters of arms and power than he was with any intellectual exercise. Of a family of rich Florentine merchants, Urban, now answerable to no one but himself, saw an open field into which his pride and vanity could expand. In the six long audiences with the Pope, Galileo gathered the impression that the decree against him was a legalistic church affair and that Copernicus, who had been chosen by Pope Gregory to help in the reformation of the calendar, could therefore not have held heretical ideas. Therefore Urban allowed the astronomer to continue in his speculations (the exact records of the audiences have been lost). The dialog of the two men, one trained in the humanism of his time and in the discipline of his church, the other exposed to the excitement of the new science with its reward of understanding the complexities of the physical world; these two thought they spoke the same language but each mind created thoughts and visions of entirely different meaning.

Altho the 1616 ban on teaching Copernicanism was not lifted, the Pope did write to the Grand Duke, "The fame of which will shine on earth so long as Jupiter and his satellites shine in heaven."* Galileo left Rome in an optimistic mood and was ready to resume where he had left off eight years ago. He was now 60 years old and within him surged the wish once again to formulate his thoughts on heliocentrism.

The DIALOG is Begun

As a feeling of security rose in Galileo's consciousness with his improved personal status, his impatience to speak more loudly and firmly of the truth of the Copernican system encouraged him to take some next step. Nearly ten years had passed since the prohibitions against holding and teaching anything so controversial had been imposed on him and he was eager for another try. With Urban VIII occupying the papacy and Galileo holding a reputation as a sound astronomer, mathematician and mechanician, the latter thought long on the means by which he could advance the inevitable Copernican proposition that was sure to arouse old feuds and new antagonisms. He decided on using the literary form of dialog, a form used by Plato. This would enable him to present all of the arguments pro and

---

*SINGER, C., *Studies in the History of Science*, Oxford, 1921, Vol. 2, p. 258.

Galileo, *Dialogo, Massimi Sistemi*, 1632

The dialog on the two main systems of the world are represented in this engraved title of Galileo's book. Aristotle and Ptolemy are shown on the left and Copernicus, right, holds a representation of his heliocentric system. The book was to introduce the new astronomy on a more popular level but in spite of its clearance by the censors, it remained on the Index from 1633 to 1822.

con of both the Ptolemaic and the Copernican systems so that the reader would himself weigh the arguments and arrive at his own conclusions. Such an impartial approach would, he thought, disarm his critics and leave Galileo innocent of the charge of protagonism. Salviati* would discourse on the Copernican system, Simplicio on the Ptolemaic and Aristotelian systems. The third person, Sagredo,** was the intelligent man in the street who asked the leading questions.

From 1625 to 1629 Galileo wove his dialog into statement, proof and argument about the cosmos. In spite of the interruptions of ill health and the distractions of engineering commissions, the general form of his *Dialog* began to take shape. He realized that the times and circumstances permitted no error. By the end of 1629 the text of the book was completed.

The book was intended to report four days of such dialog; by 1630 he felt that it was in presentable form. Galileo now faced the delicate process of obtaining an imprimatur and he felt that the setting was favorable. In addition to the friendly Pope,

the chief licensing authority, Father Niccolò Riccardi, was also a friend of Galileo. The good Father's cosmic views were exceedingly simple (the planets were directed in their courses by angels), beside which the involvements of either Ptolemy or Copernicus left him unmoved.

Galileo again journeyed to Rome, taking his manuscript with him. He was optimistic and expected the grant of the imprimatur without much difficulty. Some revisions were requested and these were readily made, but with each additional step greater doubt rose in Riccardi's mind and he played for time. He requested further revisions but Galileo argued him out of them, tho not without new difficulties arising.

The plague then broke out in Rome, and Prince Cesi, who had intended to publish the book in Rome for the Lincean Academy, died. Galileo was advised to have the book printed in Florence but not without Riccardi's revised preface and a conclusion. Accordingly, the Inquisitor at Florence was requested to pass on the publication. More arguments and hesitation; the Pope's views were reconsidered and finally in June 1631 printing began; in February 1632 the *Dialog** appeared. The long delay in readying the *Dialog* for the press had whetted the appetites of its potential readers so that when it finally appeared the entire edition was sold out as it left the bindery.

---

* Filippo Salviati (1582–1614) of a noble Florentine family had also studied under Galileo at Padua. Galileo wrote his book on *Sunspots* while at Salviati's villa at Signa near Florence; it was dedicated to his host. Galileo nominated Salviati to the Accademia dei Lincei. He often used Salviati to speak his own thoughts in the *Dialog*.

** Giovanni Francesco Sagredo (1571–1629), a Venetian who studied under Galileo at Padua and became his closest friend. Wealthy and influential, he helped and advised Galileo, warning him against leaving the free atmosphere of Venice for the constraints of Tuscany. Sagredo was said also to have made some creditable researches in magnetism and, while on a mission to Aleppo in Syria where he represented the Republic of Venice, he determined the magnetic declination of that city. (See MOTTELAY, P. F., *Bibliographical History of Electricity and Magnetism*, London, 1922, p. 116). In the *Dialog* he speaks as an educated layman and neutral observer won over to Copernicanism.

---

* An English translation by Thomas Salusbury appeared in London in 1661. Two scholarly modern English versions are:
GALILEO GALILEI, *Dialogue Concerning the Two Chief World Systems—Ptolemaic and Copernican* translated by Stillman Drake, foreword by Albert Einstein, Berkeley, 1953.
GALILEO GALILEI, *Dialogue on the Great World Systems, in the Salusbury Translation, Revised, Annotated and with an Introduction by Giorgio de Santillana*, Chicago, 1953.

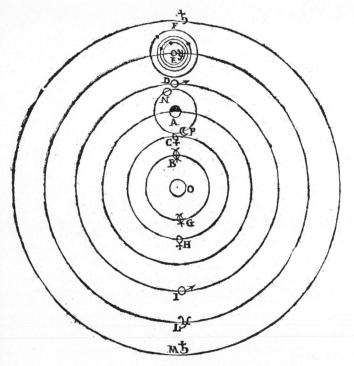

Galileo, *Dialogo, Massimi Sistemi*, 1632

Using the famous engraving with which Copernicus in 1543 introduced his concept of the heliocentric universe, Galileo in his *Dialog* showed Jupiter being circled by the four satellites which he was the first to see.

The dialog of the first day introduced the Aristotelian concept of motion and a discussion of the moon. The second day discussed diurnal rotation under the Copernican system and here the various arguments on "the detached body" are reviewed. The return of arrows or cannon balls shot vertically upward, the path of shot fired east and west having equal or unequal trajectories, and many other controversies were discussed.

Toward the end of the day Galileo injected a pertinent story from which one may draw many inferences. He has Sagredo say, "This reminds me of a man who wanted to

sell me a secret method of communicating with a person two or three thousand miles away, by means of a certain sympathy of magnetic needles. I told him that I would gladly buy, but wanted to see by experiment and that it would be enough for me if he would stand in one room and I in another. He replied that its operation could not be detected at such a short distance. I sent him on his way, with the remark that I was not in the mood at that time to go to Cairo or Moscow for the experiment, but that if he wanted to go I would stay in Venice and take care of the other end."

The third day is devoted to assessing the annual motion in terms of the Copernican universe which was found logical, the Ptolemaic inconsistent. The simplicity of the Copernican system was ranged against the complexity of the Ptolemaic.

Galileo on Magnetism

It is in the third day that Galileo uses the magnetic argument of William Gilbert for whom Galileo expressed much admiration. It was also this dialog for which Galileo had reserved his heaviest ammunition. Each argument was raised, carefully considered and answered with logic, observation and analogy. Said Salviati, "We shall next consider the annual movement generally attributed to the sun, but then, first by Aristarchos of Samos and later by Copernicus, removed from the sun and transferred to the earth. Against this position I know that Simplicio comes strongly armed, in particular with the sword and buckler of his booklet of these or mathematical disquisitions. It will be good to commence by producing the objections from this booklet."

He continues, "But now let Simplicio begin to set forth those objections which restrain him from believing that the earth, like the other planets, may revolve about a fixed center."*

The argument continues and turns to what exists in nature and the limits of man's awareness of what there is and what there may be. Sagredo argues, "Besides, what does it mean to say that the space between Saturn and the fixed stars, which these men call too vast and useless, is empty of world bodies? That we do not see them, perhaps? Then did the four satellites of Jupiter and the companions of Saturn come into the heavens when we began seeing them, and not before? Were there not innumerable other fixed stars before men began to see them? The nebulae were once only little white patches; have we with our telescopes made them become clusters of many bright and beautiful stars? Oh, the presumptuous, rash ignorance of mankind!"**

The argument returns to the failure to observe stellar parallax. Every Copernican felt that if the stars' parallax could be established, it would confirm the orbital rotation of the earth beyond all doubt. And yet such parallax had not been observed. Said Salviati, "I wish you had said that if such a variation were perceived, nothing would remain that could cast doubt upon the earth's mobility, since no counter could be found to such an event . . . As a matter of fact, how would you expect anyone to be sure, with a quadrant or sextant that customarily has an arm three or four yards long, that he is not out by two or three minutes in the setting of the perpendicular or the alignment of the

alidade? For on such a circumference this will be no more than the thickness of a millet seed. Besides which, it is almost impossible for the instrument to be constructed absolutely accurate and then maintained so. Ptolemy distrusted an armillary instrument constructed by Archimedes himself for determining the entry of the sun into the equinox."*

To a mind like Galileo's, trained in quantitative values, the revolution of the universe around the earth presented an entirely different concept than the system in which the earth spun daily as it moved around the sun. The *Dialog* accepts either hypothesis as a possible one to explain the appearances but when reduced to realities the latter was more plausible than the former. Considering the velocities of motion of the planets it was known that the moon, the body nearest to the earth, completed its orbit in 28 days, Mars in two years, Jupiter in 12 years, and the most distant planet, Saturn, in 30 years. Yet the geocentric system expected the most distant stars to sweep around the earth in only 24 hours! But to those who were in a position to make judgment these abstractions made little difference. Their training was in theology and law and the real world was adequately described in Scripture and Commentaries. Against these even the younger and more venturesome clerics among them were helpless.

Galileo then entered into a discussion on the two motions of the earth around the sun —the diurnal spin on its axis and the annual rotation about the sun. The polar tilt of twenty-three and one-half degrees was explained as tho the earth's axis described a

---

* DRAKE's edition of the *Dialogue*, p. 318.
** DRAKE, *Dialogue*, p. 368

---

* DRAKE, *Dialogue*, p. 387

cylinder with its bases set in the fixed stars. Precession was disregarded at that time as "a small variation in many thousands of years." Galileo's orbital motions were circular; the elliptical orbits of Kepler were disregarded (whether for the sake of simplicity in an already complex presentation, to avoid association with the Protestant Kepler, or as a matter of conviction).

In his long presentation Salviati then came to "But what will Simplicio say if, to this independence of any cooperating cause, we add a remarkable force inhering in the terrestrial globe and making it point with definite parts of itself toward definite parts of the firmament? I am speaking of magnetic force, in which every piece of lodestone constantly participates. And if every tiny particle of such stone has in it such a force, who can doubt that the same force resides to a still higher degree within the whole of this terrene globe, which abounds in this material? Or that perhaps the globe itself is, as to its internal and primary substance, nothing but an immense mass of lodestone?

SIMPLICIO: Then you are one of those people who adhere to the magnetic philosophy of William Gilbert?

SALVIATI: Certainly I am, and I believe that I have for company every man who has attentively read his book* and carried out his experiments. Nor am I without hope that what has happened to me in this regard may happen to you also, whenever a curiosity similar to mine, and a realization that numberless things in nature remain unknown to the human intellect, frees you from slavery to one particular writer or an-

other on the subject of natural phenomena, thereby slackening the reins on your reasoning and softening your stubborn defiance of your senses, so that some day you will not deny them by giving ear to voices which are heard no more."

"Now, the cowardice (if we may be permitted to use this term) of ordinary minds has gone to such lengths that not only do they blindly make a gift—nay, a tribute—of their own assent to everything they find written by those authors who were lauded by their teachers in the first infancy of their studies, but they refuse even to listen to, let alone examine, any new proposition or problem, even when it not only has not been refuted by their authorities, but not so much as examined or considered. One of these problems is the investigation of what is the true, proper, basic, internal, and general matter and substance of this terrestrial globe of ours. Even though neither Aristotle nor anybody else before Gilbert ever took it into his head to consider whether this substance might be lodestone (let alone Aristotle or anybody else having disproved such an opinion), I have met many who have started back at the first hint of this like a horse at his shadow, and avoided discussing such an idea, making it out to be a vain hallucination, or rather a mighty madness. And perhaps Gilbert's book would never have come into my hands if a famous Peripatetic philosopher had not made me a present of it, I think in order to protect his library from its contagion."* Salviati then added "And if it must be such, what reason have you for being more reluctant to believe that it is lodestone than that it is por-

---

* GILBERT, William, *De Magnete*, London, 1600.

* DRAKE, *Dialogue*, p. 399, 402.

phyry, jasper, or some other hard stone? If Gilbert had written that the inside of this globe is made of sandstone, or chalcedony, perhaps the paradox would seem less strange to you?"

Continuing his argument, Salviati goes on for a dozen pages until the end of the Third Day expanding on Gilbert's suggestion that the earth was a giant lodestone. He had said on the First Day, "From which it is obvious that the moon, as if drawn by a magnetic force, faces the earth constantly with one surface and never deviates in this regard." His companions were invited to read Gilbert's book and to become conversant with the properties of magnets, repeating the more significant experiments. Attraction, variation, dip and the unique properties of the lodestone as described by Gilbert were reviewed. Sagredo indicated that after having read Gilbert's book he learned to provide an iron armature covering the pole ends of a lodestone with a cap of thin iron and thus multiplied the magnetic strength eight-fold. Sagredo later sold his lodestone with armatures to the Grand Duke, a complex transaction in which Galileo became involved. It is indicated that Galileo (referred to in the text as "our Academician"*) himself had increased the attractive power of a lodestone weighing six ounces to support 26 times its own weight when equipped with an armature. Galileo had made additional observations on the lodestone in 1607**.

Word of these experiments reached Prince Cosimo who let it be known that he would like to acquire Galileo's half-pound (Tuscan) lodestone. Negotiations followed, not for Galileo's lodestone, but for one that Galileo said was much more desirable, that belonged to an acquaintance (it was Sagredo), for which he had been offered 200 gold crowns by a German jeweler, but that its price was 400 crowns. The price gap was closed after four months' bargaining; the agreed price was 100 gold crowns.

Mention is made* of a gift of a lodestone by Galileo to the Grand Duke Ferdinando II that was described by Castelli in his "Discorso sopra la Calamita" wherein "I have seen a small stone only 6 ounces in weight, armed with iron by the exquisite diligence of Signor Galileo, and presented by him to the Most Serene Grand Duke, which holds suspended 15 pounds of iron, worked in the form of a sepulchre." This stone was on display in the Tribuna di Galileo in Florence still supporting its iron burden. The coffin shape given to the load stems from the legend that Mohammed's coffin hung in mid-air by the magnetic influence of lodestones.

Gilbert's book, by its systematic observation of every phase of magnetic action that its author thought of and experimented with, established him as the first important experimental scientist in England. Galileo as an experimenter himself responded to such a novel approach. He therefore wrote, thru Salviati, "I have the highest praise, admiration, and envy for this author, who framed such a stupendous concept regarding an object which innumerable men of splendid intellect had handled without paying any attention to it. He seems to me

---

* Galileo was a member of the Accademia dei Lincei (an academy of "Lynxes" or sharp-eyed), founded in Rome in 1603 by Prince Federico Cesi, whom Galileo befriended. Galileo was proud of being a Linceo.

** DRAKE, *Dialogue*, p. 488.

* FAHIE, J. J., *Galileo and Magnetism: A Study in Lodestones*, Jnl. I.E.E., April 1918, pp. 246–249.

worthy of great acclaim also for the many new and sound observations which he made, to the shame of the many foolish and mendacious authors who write not just what they know, but also all the vulgar foolishness they hear, without trying to verify it by experiment; perhaps they do this in order not to diminish the size of their books. What I might have wished for in Gilbert would be a little more of the mathematician, and especially a thorough grounding in geometry, a discipline which would have rendered him less rash about accepting as rigorous proofs those reasons which he puts forward as *verae causae* for the correct conclusions he himself had observed. His reasons, candidly speaking, are not rigorous, and lack that force which must unquestionably be present in those adduced as necessary and eternal scientific conclusions." . . .

"Now, in answer to your question, I say that I also thought for a long time to find the cause for this tenacious and powerful connection that we see between the iron armature of a lodestone and the other iron which joins itself to it. In the first place, I am certain that the power and force of the stone is not increased at all by its having an armature, for it does not attract through a longer distance. Nor does it attract a piece of iron as strongly if a thin slip of paper is introduced between this and the armature; even if a piece of gold leaf is interposed, the bare lodestone will sustain more iron than the armature. Hence there is no change here in the force, but merely something new in its effect."

"And since for a new effect there must be a new cause, we seek what is newly introduced by the act of supporting the iron via the armature, and no other change is to be found than a difference in contact. For where iron originally touched lodestone, now iron touches iron, and it is necessary to conclude that the difference in these contacts causes the difference in the results. Next, the difference between the contacts must come, so far as I can see, from the substance of the iron being finer, purer, and denser in its particles than is that of the lodestone, whose parts are coarser, less pure, and less dense. From this it follows that the surfaces of the two pieces of iron which are to touch, when perfectly smoothed, polished, and burnished, fit together so exactly that all the infinity of points on one touch the infinity of points on the other. Thus the threads which unite the pieces of iron are, so to speak, more numerous than those which join lodestone to iron, on account of the substance of lodestone being more porous and less integrated, so that not all the points and threads on the surface of the iron find counterparts to unite with on the surface of the lodestone."

"Now we may see that the substance of iron (especially when much refined, as is the finest steel) is much more dense, fine, and pure in its particles than is the material of lodestone, from the possibility of bringing the former to an extremely thin edge, such as a razor edge, which can never be done to a piece of lodestone with any success. The impurity of the lodestone and its adulteration with other kinds of stone can next be sensibly observed; in the first place by the color of some little spots, gray for the most part, and secondly by bringing it near a needle suspended on a thread. The needle cannot come to rest at these little stony places; it is attracted by the surrounding

Meyer, C.; *Nuovi Ritrovamenti*, Roma, 1696

Natural magnets, or lodestones, were much studied by academies and prized by peers.
The large lodestone in the Galleria of the Grand Duke in Florence is shown supporting
a weight of 55 Tuscan pounds. The large lodestone, right, rested in the courtyard of the
ducal palace.

portions, and appears to leap toward these and flee from the former spots. And since some of these heterogeneous spots are large enough to be easily visible, we may believe that others are scattered in great quantity throughout the mass but are not noticeable because of their small size."

"What I am telling you (that is, that the great abundance of contacts made between iron and iron is the cause of so solid an attachment) is confirmed by an experiment. If we present the sharp point of a needle to the armature of a lodestone, it attaches itself no more strongly than it would to the bare lodestone; this can result only from the two contacts being equal, both being made at a single point. But now see what follows. A needle is placed upon the lodestone so that one of its ends sticks out somewhat beyond, and a nail is brought up to this. Instantly the needle will attach itself to it so firmly that upon the nail being drawn back, the needle can be suspended with one end attached to the lodestone and the other to the nail. Withdrawing the nail still farther, the needle will come loose from the lodestone if the needle's eye is attached to the nail and its point to the lodestone; but if the eye is toward the lodestone, the needle will remain attached to the lodestone upon withdrawing the nail. In my judgment, this is for no other reason than that the needle, being larger at the eye, makes contact in more places than it does at its very sharp point."

SAGREDO: "The entire argument looks convincing to me, and I rank these experiments with the needle very little lower than mathematical proof. I frankly admit that in the entire magnetic science I have not heard or read anything which gives so cogently the reasons for any of its other remarkable phenomena." . . .

SALVIATI: "Wishing to assure myself by some other observation that the cause I had turned up was correct (that is, that the substance of the lodestone really was much less continuous than that of iron or steel), I had the artisans who work in the museum of my lord the Grand Duke smooth for me one face of that same piece of lodestone which was formerly yours, and then polish and burnish it as much as possible. To my great satisfaction, this enabled me to experience directly just what I sought. For there I found many spots of different color from the rest, bright and shiny as any very dense, hard stone; the rest of the field was polished only to the touch, being not the least bit shiny, but rather as if covered with mist. This was the substance of the lodestone, and the shiny parts were of other stones mixed with it, as was sensibly recognized by bringing the smooth face toward some iron filings, which leaped in large quantities to the lodestone. But not a single grain went to the spots mentioned, of which there were many, some as large as a quarter of a fingernail, some rather smaller, and many quite small; those which were scarcely visible were almost innumerable."

"Thus was I assured that my idea had been quite correct when I first judged that the substance of the lodestone must be not continuous and compact, but porous. Better yet, spongy; though with this difference: where the cavities and cells of a sponge contain air or water, those of the lodestone are filled with hard and heavy stone, as shown by the high lustre that they take on. Whence, as I said at the outset, upon applying the surface of iron to the surface of a lodestone, the minute particles of iron— though continuous in perhaps a greater degree than those of any other material, as shown by their shining more than any other material,—do not all meet solid lodestone, but only a few of them; and the contacts being few, the attachment is weak. But the armature of a lodestone, in addition to touching a large part of its surface, is also vested with the force of the closer parts even though not touching them; and being quite flat on the side applied to the suspended iron (this also being well smoothed), contact is made by innumerable tiny particles if not by the infinity of points on both surfaces, which yields a very strong attachment."*

This seeming concern with minutiae was really the continuation of careful scientific experimenting and observing of the magnet that Gilbert had established. Galileo's book followed by 30 years that of Gilbert, the first attempt at objectivity and thoroness in the study of magnetic phenomena. Galileo, however, was here concerned with magne-

*DRAKE, *Dialogue*, pp. 407–409.

tism only as a means to describing an operating world system with its complex of bodies and forces in interplay. Salviati was therefore prompted to say, "Let us add next, to this simple and natural event, the magnetic force by which the terrestrial globe may be kept so much the more solidly immutable, etc. . . ."

SAGREDO: "What I wanted to bring up for consideration was precisely the lodestone, to which three movements are sensibly seen to belong naturally: One toward the center of the earth as a heavy object; a second is the horizontal circular motion by which it restores and conserves its axis in the direction of certain parts of the universe; and third is this one discovered by Gilbert*, of dipping its axis in the meridian plane toward the surface of the earth, in greater or less degree proportionate to its distance from the equator (where it remains parallel to the axis of the earth). Besides these three, it is perhaps not improbable that it may have a fourth motion of turning about its own axis, whenever it is balanced and suspended in air or some other fluid and yielding medium and all external and accidental impediments are taken away; Gilbert himself also shows his approval of this idea. So you see, Simplicio, how shaky Aristotle's axiom is." . . .

SAGREDO: "Wait a moment, Simplicio. Answer the questions I am going to ask you. You say that the lodestone is not a simple body, but a compound one; now I ask you what are the simple bodies which are mixed in the compounding of lodestone?"

SIMPLICIO: "I cannot tell you the ingredients or the exact proportions, but it is sufficient

that they are elementary bodies."

The dialog continued and was summed up by Salviati when he said, "Sagredo, please let us weary ourselves no longer with these particulars, especially since you know that our goal is not to judge rashly or accept as true either one opinion or the other, but merely to set forth for our own pleasure those arguments and counterarguments which can be adduced for one side and for the other. Simplicio answers thus in order to rescue his Peripatetics; therefore we shall suspend judgment and leave this in the hands of whoever knows more about it than we do."

Pertinent to our subject, Salviati adds, "Meanwhile, lest I forget, I want to tell you about one particular to which I wish Gilbert had not lent his ear. This is his concession that if a small sphere of lodestone were exactly balanced, it would revolve upon itself; for this no cause whatever exists. For if the entire terrestrial globe has by its nature a rotation about its own center every twenty-four hours, and all its parts must also rotate together with the whole around its center in twenty-four hours, then by being on the earth they already actually have this motion, turning together with the earth, and to assign to them a motion around their own centers would be to attribute to them a second movement quite different from the first. Thus they would have two motions; that is, a rotation in twenty-four hours about the center of the whole, and a revolution upon their own centers. Now this second motion is arbitrary, and there is no reason whatever for introducing it. If, upon becoming detached from the whole natural mass, a piece of lodestone were deprived of the property of following that mass as it did while they were joined together (so that

---

* This attribution is in error. Magnetic dip of the compass needle was first reported by Robert Norman in England in 1576.

it would be deprived of the revolution about the universal center of the terrestrial globe), there might perhaps be a greater probability for believing that it would take upon itself a new whirling about its own particular center. But if it always continues its original natural and perpetual course whether separated or attached, then to what purpose would another new one be added?"

The subject of the dialog then turned to the behavior of water and the tides, the theme of the Fourth Day.

Tides, like magnetism, were phenomena of action at a distance, the one gravitational, the other magnetic. Whereas the *Dialog* set out to be primarily concerned with tides, it changed as Galileo expanded his subject and the Pope's opinions became involved. Further, altho Galileo felt he had a major contribution to make in the theory of the tides, his position suffered from two important shortcomings. His first-hand experience in tides was limited to the Mediterranean where they are minimal and not important. He therefore depended on data supplied by others, much of it quite unreliable. The second handicap in formulating a sound theory of tide was his leaning towards the transfer of force between bodies by some form of intimate contact rather than what evolved into the "field theory" of the 19th and 20th centuries. He therefore built up his theory of tides not from external attraction but from the inside out, so to speak. He held that the oceans rested on a revolving earth also circling the sun and it was this double motion that imparted to the waters their three periods of tidal motion—the daily, monthly and annual components. The behavior of magnetic attraction was manifest in his laboratory but the tides were quite speculative. Thru

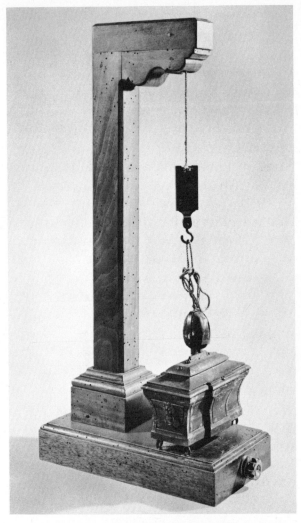

Museo di Storia della Scienza, Firenze

One of Galileo's lodestones demonstrates its high holding power. The suspended iron weight is coffin shaped to commemorate the myth of Mahommed's magnetically suspended coffin.

Salviati he even brushed aside Kepler's support of the notion that it was lunar attraction that influenced the tides.

The DIALOG is Stopped

Having hastily scanned the contents of the *Dialog* we now turn to a short review of what happened to the book and its author. This is an oft-told tale but, like the Christmas Story or what happened at Salamis or at Gettysburg, it is one that shall continue to be retold forever. It was the turning point from one long and important era in human thought and society into another only three centuries old but fundamentally different (and considerably more welcome).

Galileo had every reason to be proud and satisfied when his *Dialog* issued from the Florence press and was ready for the reader. Pope Urban VIII was friendly to Galileo and had shown himself liberal with new doctrines. The imprimatur had been obtained and whatever difficulties had arisen had each been finally overcome. The book was now in the hands of the learned and its very contents were to arouse two diametrically opposed courses of action. Those who admired its line of reasoning and its conclusions applauded its author with enthusiasm. Those who saw in the message of the *Dialog* a presentation that questioned and scorned tradition and authority felt they had to act if their authority were to survive. This called for extreme measures, for there could be no middle ground.

It took from February to June for a sufficient number of books to be carried from Florence to Rome but by then the lines of reaction were set. The Jesuits and Dominicans joined in the offensive against their position and prerogatives. The Jesuits, as those charged with the mission of education, felt especially sensitive to this challenge on what they held sacred. It was a surprised Galileo who learned in August that the sale of the book had been ordered stopped. Galileo's prepared defenses proved less firm than he had planned.

The timing of the appearance of the *Dia-*

log found the nerves of Urban on raw edge. He had been suffering a series of political and military reverses in the Thirty Years War, the culmination of failure of his many involved plans, intrigues and maneuvers. He was in no mood for insubordination at home, and the Jesuits made the most of it. The privilege of the entire educational system administered by the Jesuits seemed now in jeopardy. The Pope was angry at what was told him, but so was Galileo angry. Galileo felt he had in complete honesty responded to an implied invitation to present the case for and against heliocentrism and had done so within the bounds that had been outlined to him. He had presented all the pertinent arguments and had done so not to weaken Scripture but to reinforce it in the light of new realities. The argument had been presented not as his, but from the mouths of those holding varying opinions. He had patiently gathered the required licenses and endorsements before submitting the text to the printer; two imprimaturs bearing five signatures crowded the title leaf. He had agreed to changes and revisions, and more changes and more revisions by authorities in Florence as well as in Rome. He had added a suggested preface and changed the ending as well as the title as had been indicated by the Pope himself.

Galileo had felt that within the bounds set for him, Urban would be swayed by the logic and honesty of his presentation, the bond of friendship built between them over the years and by the recent show of tolerance to Tommaso Campanella, an opponent of scholasticism and Aristotle and an open supporter of Copernicus. Campanella had been kept in prison for 27 years on heresy charges by the Spanish lords of Naples. Whether the miscalculation by Galileo

Robert-Fleury, N-D, Giraudon, Louvre, Paris

Galileo is forced to deny any support for a heliocentric world before the Inquisition in
Rome, as seen by an artist. Altho 70 years old, the decree issued against him placed him
on permanent house arrest and put his *Dialog* on the Index.

might have been his lusty optimism, his vanity or his faith in rational treatment, he now became aware of his predicament.

On the other hand, the imprimatur of the church authorities was considered fraudulently obtained. An appeal from the Grand Duke Ferdinand to the Pope received little attention. A visit by the Tuscan ambassador to the Pope found Urban angry, repeating that the imprimatur had been gotten thru deception and that the contents of the book were no hypothetical discussion but the ad-

vancement of a theory against the support of which Galileo had been specifically warned 16 years earlier.

As a move of clemency toward Galileo, the Pope did not condemn the book openly nor place it directly before the Inquisition but appointed a special commission to examine the offending book. What was not so clear was that the commission was composed of members antagonistic to Galileo. In its proceedings Galileo was not examined nor represented, the charges were not placed before him and the investigation was carried on in complete secrecy. Their report was issued in a month.

From September to December 1632 events moved quickly. The sale of the book was suspended and Galileo was ordered by the Pope to appear before the Commissary-General. The Inquisition would tolerate no more the "subterfuges" by Galileo that kept him from Rome, and demanded his immediate appearance. He reminded them of his former and present submission, his continued piety, his daughters who had taken the veil, his contrition. The Pope remained adamant. Three doctors in a report detailed Galileo's serious physical and mental illnesses and advised against the hazards of a journey to Rome. But the Pope was still adamant and ordered Galileo brought to Rome as a prisoner in irons if further delays were incurred. The Grand Duke (then only 22) felt it the better part of wisdom to have Galileo submit. After the initial debilitating shock Galileo recovered some of his fighting spirit and decided to face his tormentors.

With the memory of Giordano Bruno given to the flames in the Campo di Fiori in Rome in 1600, Galileo felt trapped and in deep despair. He wrote to a friend, "I not only repent having given the world a portion of my writings, but feel inclined to suppress those still in hand, and to give them to the flames, and thus satisfy the longing desire of my enemies to whom my ideas are so inconvenient."*

A broken Galileo left by litter for Rome in February 1633. It required 23 days for him to reach Rome, to rest at the Tuscan embassy and to prepare for the accusations

*Quoted in MACDONNELL, Sir John, *Historical Trials*, Oxford 1927, pp. 123, 126.

against him. In April the Inquisition began its examination. The sanguine Galileo, in defense, took the position that he had been given to understand by Cardinal Bellarmin in 1616 that he had not agreed to refrain from teaching the Copernican doctrine but had committed himself not to hold or to defend it. Pressure continued on him and he was forced to abjectly recant, willing to assert that the earth did stand still and the sun revolved. He pleaded that the passage of many years and faulty memory had dimmed his earlier agreement. The inquisitors pressed on and Galileo retreated further.

Before the Inquisition

Five days after the Inquisitors' examination, a special report by the three Counselors of the Inquisition was rendered. It held that Galileo had indeed taught, defended and held the Copernican thesis. The report stated, further, that Galileo favored the arguments for heliocentrism and scorned those who doubted it. Galileo's praise of the "perverse heretic", William Gilbert, clearly showed his bias. The seventy-year old accused was provided with comfortable enough quarters but was then suffering from hernial disorders, sciatic pains and intestinal difficulties that still seemed to him more bearable than the stone wall of mystery, silence and enmity that he faced during the weeks that the Inquisitors were deliberating.

The commission found the contents of the book offensive on eight counts and Galileo guilty on three counts. The first held Galileo guilty of advocating the fixed position of the sun and the mobility of the earth not as an hypothesis but as a doctrine. From the above he had deduced falsely the motion of the tides. Finally he had held, contrary to command of the Holy Office imposed upon him in 1616 prohibiting him "to hold, teach, or defend in any way whatever, verbally or in writing", the opinion that the sun was the center of the world and that the earth moved. That the book was written in the common tongue, Italian, rather than in Latin, made it more offensive because this would even further spread the obnoxious doctrine.

On 12 April Galileo was called before the authorities and in the proceedings reviewed the conditions that had led to the injunction of 1616 and the more recent action by the Inquisition. At a second hearing, on 30 April, Galileo stated he had been shown a copy of his *Dialog*, a book he had not seen for three years, and reviewed it minutely for any deviations that inadvertantly might have slipped into the text. Admitting to a possible overzeal in his attempt to be impartial in the dialog and to weigh all sides equally (thereby exhibiting undue vanity and ambition), he later suggested being allowed to continue the dialog for an additional day or two; this flowed naturally from the trio's agreement, at the published book's end, that they were to meet again to continue their discourse.

Galileo was summoned before the Holy Office for sentencing on 21 June 1633. On inquiry as to which opinion he held regarding the world system, he replied that he had once held both systems as open to discussion but on the decision of the Holy Congregation, "I held, as I still hold, as most true and indisputable, the opinion of Ptolemy, that is to say, the stability of the Earth and the motion of the Sun." He repeated that he had presented the *Dialog* as an exercise

in argument and not as an expression of conviction. Pressed further, he repeated, "I do not hold and have not held this opinion of Copernicus since the command was intimated to me that I must abandon it; for the rest, I am here in your hands—do with me what you please."*

On the following day, wearing the white shirt of penitence and kneeling before his ten Cardinal judges in the Dominican convent of Santa Maria sopra Minerva, he listened to the sentence imposed on him. His guilt in holding that the Sun was the center of the world, that the Earth moved, in teaching such to disciples, in having correspondence with mathematicians in Germany, in having disregarded the injunction of 1616 —so began a long list of particulars against Galileo. A new book (the *Dialog*) based on false ground was then published counter to Cardinal Bellarmin's command. A license to publish was obtained without mention of the injunction, but a certificate of defense against the calumnies of his enemies, written by Bellarmin, was handily produced when the limits of the injunction were questioned. Now, from the evidence against him and his own confessions, he was found vehemently suspected of heresy and therefore must suffer the penalties and censures of such guilt. The *Dialog* was prohibited** and Galileo was condemned to the formal prison of the Holy Office and for three years was to repeat the seven penitential psalms once a week.

The sentence by his judges was lengthy and specific, beginning, "Whereas you, Galileo, son of the late Vincenzo Galilei, Florentine, aged 70 years, were in the year 1615

---

* de SANTILLANA, *Crime of Galileo*, pp. 302, 303.
** The book remained on the Index until 1822.

denounced to this Holy Office for holding as true the false doctrine taught by many, that the sun is the center of the world and immovable and that the earth moves, and also with a diurnal motion; . . ." and "by reason of the matters adduced in process, and by you confessed as above, have rendered yourself in the judgment of this Holy Office vehemently suspected of heresy—namely, of having believed and held the doctrine—which is false and contrary to the sacred and divine Scriptures—that the sun is the center of the world and does not move from east to west, and that the earth moves and is not the center of the world; . . ."* It was signed by seven of the ten judge Cardinals.

Galileo faced his judges, kneeled and recanted his opinions in a lengthy statement. He regretted his heretical depravity and asserted that he always believed, and will for the future believe, all that was held and taught by the Church. "But whereas—after an injunction had been judicially intimated to me by this Holy Office, to the effect that I must altogether abandon the false opinion that the sun is the center of the world and immovable, and that the earth is not the center of the world, and moves, and that I must not hold, defend, or teach in any way whatsoever, verbally or in writing, the said doctrine, and after it had been notified to me that the said doctrine was contrary to Holy Scripture—I wrote and printed a book. . . ."

Then came his recantation—"With sincere heart and unfeigned faith I abjure, curse and detest the aforesaid errors and heresies, and generally every other error and sect whatsoever contrary to the said

Holy Church; and I swear that in future I will never again say or assert, verbally or in writing, anything that might furnish occasion for a similar suspicion regarding me; but that should I know any heretic, or person suspected of heresy, I will denounce him to this Holy Office, or to the Inquisitor and ordinary of the place where I may be." Galileo had emptied the bitter cup of humiliation and no physical torture or dungeon was necessary.*

After the Sentence

The intent of the Inquisitors was completed when the sentence against Galileo was read in public places everywhere in the Catholic world. Students and professors in the faculties of mathematics and philosophy at the universities were assembled and the humiliation brought upon Galileo was made clear to them. Within the discipline of his faith Galileo knew that obedience to the decision of the Pope regarding the moving Earth was unavoidable, for obey he must. As to what he was certain of in his own mind, that was his own affair and not subject to threat or bargain. There was no compromise with any moral principle, there was only public disgrace and, to one of his years, his circle of many friends and his record of accomplishments, it was indeed a deep pain. But such a mind and will were not to be compromised and he would continue to do things his way. The Florence of Dante, Lorenzo, Leonardo and Michelangelo was to be no more. Its mind had become constrained.

---

* TAYLOR, pp. 161, 167–169.

* Tradition has it that on rising to his feet, the shattered Galileo muttered "Eppur si muove", and yet it moves! However old this story may be, or how probable, it ever remains associated with that unfortunate occasion.

With sentence imposed, there was no need physically to imprison Galileo. The old man was committed to the Villa Medici where now a marble shaft proclaims his confinement there for having been "guilty of having seen the earth revolve around the sun".* To some of the interrogators the plight of Galileo was an opportunity to improve their positions in the rivalries between Jesuits and Dominicans, between Rome and Florence and between individuals within the hierarchy. With proceedings under strictest secrecy and apparent tampering with the documentation, what transpired verbally at Galileo's trial will never be fully known. With severe punishments as a penalty, one kept one's opinions to one's self, yet the Galileo case cried from, as Galileo noted**, a masterly conspiracy of "hatred, impiety, fraud and deceit". Yet remarks were let slip in confidence. The community of science and letters had its mental reservations and in the manner of the times the correspondence went from savant to savant with each point argued and exceptions taken. Descartes, Mersenne, Castelli, Peiresc, Piccolomini wrote to each other, and of course Galileo wrote to many of them.

One such letter from Father Athanasius Kircher, writing to Pierre Gassendi, said that he had told Claude de Peiresc after Ga-

lileo's trial that "He could not hold himself from admitting, in the presence of Father Ferrant, that Father Malapertius and Father Clavius himself did not really disapprove of the opinion of Copernicus; in fact, that they were not far from it themselves, although they had been pressed and ordered to write in favor of the common doctrine of Aristotle, and that Father Scheiner himself followed only by order and through obedience."* Peiresc had tried to reconcile Father Christopher Scheiner and Galileo, but the former's claim to priority in the sunspots dispute showed him in a sinister light to Peiresc. Peiresc also wrote to Dupuy on 30 May 1633 "If anyone could have merited it (prison) for the issue of his *Dialogues* it ought to be those who in their position have suppressed them. Since he has remitted it all at their discretion . . . I think that these Fathers can proceed in good faith but they will have difficulty in persuading the world of it."* Peiresc repeated this in a letter to Cardinal Francesco Barberini a year later.

The introduction of Galileo's *Dialog* and the intense drama of conflict on a cosmic scale, the subject treated by the keenest of scholars for over three centuries, is touched on here for its pertinence to the understanding of the first paragraph of Galileo's letter which is the subject of the essay that follows. In order to understand progress or decline in some section of human society, points of reference are essential. The setting, the subject, the treatment and the outcome of the trials of Galileo, helped by comparatively ample documentation, form one such stage of reference. We owe it to science, and to history, to examine it.

---

*On the Pincian Hill overlooking Rome stands a white marble column to which a bronze plate is fastened. On it one reads:

THE ADJOINING PALACE
ONCE OF THE MEDICI
WAS THE PRISON OF GALILEO GALILEI
GUILTY OF HAVING SEEN
THE EARTH REVOLVE AROUND THE SUN

———

S. P. Q. R.
MDCCCLXXXVII

**de SANTILLANA, *Crime of Galileo*, p. 290.

---

* de SANTILLANA, *The Crime of Galileo*, pp. 290; 300.

The Aftermath

Appeals to the Pope by the Tuscan ambassador to permit the ill and disconsolate Galileo to return to his house in Arcetri, just south of Florence, were denied as being too lenient. In July he was permitted to go to Siena to remain at the palace of the Archbishop Ascanio Piccolomini where he remained for five months. With this change of setting, his restless mind resumed some of the unfinished problems that had been interrupted. He continued to receive comfort from his daughter, Virginia, (Sister Maria Celeste), a nun in Arcetri, and, in December 1633, Galileo received permission to return to his house and observatory. His reunion with his daughter was brief for she died the following April. This left Galileo quite alone. He was, by command, to remain in Arcetri, could receive only approved visitors but was forbidden to discuss matters of science.

His final work, considered by some as the most substantive, was prepared in the next few years. *Discourses Concerning Two New Sciences* was fundamentally a work of physics, stressing the dynamics of bodies in motion. In a more sober approach than his earlier *Dialog* he presented his theory of projectiles, the resistance of solid bodies to concussion and fracture, the forces of cohesion in a body, the acceleration of motion and the proof of the parabolic trajectory of ballistic missiles, then, as always, a subject of intense interest. The new *Discourses* were conducted as a dialog by the same principles as in the *Two Principal Systems of the World*—Salviati, Sagredo and Simplicio.

To avoid the unpleasantness of his former work, Galileo had the book printed in Leyden, Holland, out of the reach of censors and inquisitors. A note in the dedication "complained" that the printing had been carried out against the author's wishes. Having little concern with matters of theology, the book was disregarded by the theologians. Experiments were described that attempted to determine the velocity of light; it was concluded that the velocity was finite but too great to be measured by the means then available. Experiments in the creation of vacuum were also tried and the velocity of falling bodies discussed. The resistance and weight of air were considered as they affected falling bodies and pendulums in motion. This led to discussions about sonics, sympathetic vibration and musical ratios that correspond to simple numerical proportions. Two famous propositions concerned the strength of beams, simple and cantilever, and Galileo's attempt to determine the law of accelerated motion by letting a ball roll down an inclined plane and finding that the distance of travel was proportional to the square of the time.

In the Fourth Day of the *Discourses*, while attempting to resolve a speculation about the origin of the planets, Galileo remembered with bitterness his recent experience for he had Salviati say, "I think I do remember that he [the author] had heretofore told me that he had once made the computation, and also that he found it exactly to answer the observations: But that he had no mind to speak of them, doubting lest the too many novelties by him discovered, which had provoked the displeasure of many against him, might blow up new sparks."*

In the summer of 1637, partial blind-

*TAYLOR, pp. 189, 190.

ness further limited the range of Galileo's activities; in the following January he became completely blind. His penetrating eyes would see no more and as he wrote to a friend, "Alas, Sir, Galileo your friend and servant, has become in the last month irremediably and totally blind. You may imagine what my feelings are when I think that heaven, that universe, that I with my marvelous observations and clear demonstrations had expanded a hundred and a thousand times from what had been thought by the wise men of all past centuries, has now diminished and shrunk for me so that it is no larger than what my person can occupy."*

On Measuring Time

The need for accurate time measurement became more pressing as Galileo evolved physical, gravitational and astronomical experiments involving short periods of time. He resorted to using a dry, empty vessel of determined weight. This he placed under a large container of water having a very small orifice. To measure time, Galileo held his thumb on the orifice, released it to measure a time interval and again sealed the orifice when the interval ended. The lower vessel would then be weighed and the amount of escaped water would be compared to a table of measured water weights and time. We have already seen (page 8) his application of the pendulum principle of vibration rate to the measurement of a pulse beat.

Another pressing problem, that of determining the longitude of ships at sea, concerned Galileo as it did many of the scientists of the time. One proposal he made

----

*To Elia Diodati (1576–1661). It was in his blindness that Galileo was visited at Arcetri by the young English poet, John Milton.

was, as mentioned, to observe the simultaneous occultation of one of the satellites of Jupiter from two positions on earth and from prepared tables to supply the correction from zero longitude. This called for far too accurate observations than could be provided from an unstable ship's deck. The chronometer was the answer but that lay more than a century away. He had discovered the isochrony of the pendulum some 60 years earlier; he now thought of applying this to a clock's regulation.

The clock that Galileo describes in the Fourth Day of his *Dialog* was a "wheel clock" having an escapement which consisted of a rod with a lead weight at each end. Regulation of the clock was by shifting the weights on the rod; moving them toward the center shortened the time of an oscillation, drawing them out slowed the clock. The motive power of the clock mechanism came from a suspended weight. Galileo had determined the vibration period of a pendulum; a shorter pendulum would have a shorter period of vibration. He went into considerable detail in explaining that for any given pendulum length the period of vibration was constant no matter how widely the weight was displaced from the vertical when released to swing. Clock construction was too crude in Galileo's day for astronomical use, and it was shortly before his death that the idea of applying the pendulum to clock escapement occurred to him. Being now totally blind he described his design to his son, Vincenzio, and disciple, Viviani,who prepared a drawing of the pendulum and escape mechanism. A model based on the drawing is not known to have been made. The first successful pendulum clock is credited to Christian Huygens of Holland who applied a compound pendu-

science innovation was thereby provided, a handing down of the torch of truth. The contrast between these two men and the times they represented was well marked by Stillman Drake.* The 50 years that separated Galileo's last published book and Newton's first was a half century that turned science from a field of the enlightened reader to that of the specialist. "Galileo took pleasure in conversing with artisans and applying his science to their practical problems; Newton preferred the precisely designed experiment and the deductive application of scientific laws. While Newton spent much of his life in alchemical pursuits and theological speculations, Galileo (almost alone in his age) ridiculed the alchemists, and ventured into theology only when it encroached upon his science. Galileo was personally skilled in art, talented in music, and devoted to literature; to Newton these appear to have remained passive enjoyments. In Galileo, it is hard to say whether the qualities of the Renaissance were dominant, or those of our own scientific age. Of Newton, this question cannot even be asked."

Galileo's innovations in mechanics concerned the dynamics of motion—the law of falling bodies, the principle of inertia and the resolution of complex motions. The first theme, the law of falling bodies, not only shed light on dynamic behavior of the physical world but it broke the long grip of Aristotle. Galileo's studies in ballistics clarified the concept of inertia of moving bodies and led to the revolutionary idea that a body in uniform rectilinear motion was really the equivalent of the body being in a state of rest. This transformed the science of me-

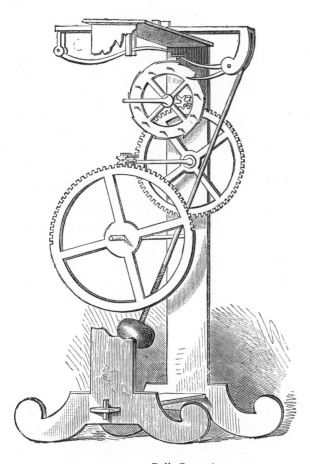

Ball, *Great Astronomers*, 1895

Design for a pendulum clock dictated by the blind Galileo and originally sketched by his son Vincenzio and pupil Viviani. The driving weight is not shown but the pendulum and escape mechanism provided isochronous timing.

lum to regulate a clock around 1657.

It has often been pointed out that Newton was born in the year that Galileo died* and that a continuum in the chain of great

---

*This was the period of transition from the Julian to the Gregorian calendar. Using the new calendar for both events, Galileo died on the evening of 8 January, 1642 and Newton was born on 5 January 1643 (old style 25 December 1642). It might be argued that the events still happened within one solar year.

---

* DRAKE, *Discoveries and Opinions of Galileo*, p. 5.

chanics from a static concept to a kinematic one and led directly to Newton's explicit formulation. The new laws also provided the mathematical support for a Copernican solar system.

Galileo died on 8 January 1642, leaving to posterity the record of a life well lived and thoroly dedicated to the search for truth in the material world. He had little faith in established authority in matters of historic and intrinsic fact. "Ancient poets, Greek philosophers, Holy Writ, were treated alike as worthless sources of information. The only source of fact was observation and experiment. He was the first to make systematic laboratory measurements of physical phenomena and to analyze these mathematically in order to reach or confirm scientific principles."*

Claude de Peiresc

The letter that Galileo sent from Arcetri, on 12 May 1635, went via Roberto Galilei (a distant relative) to Nicolas Claude Fabri de Peiresc at Lyon, France. Peiresc was one of an ancient family of Fabris that had flourished in Pisa and had moved to Aix-en-Provence in France in 1254. He was born 1 December 1580 in a chateau near Toulon. He studied the classics at Avignon, astronomy and mathematics at Tournon and history and law at Aix. His formal studies were followed by journeys to Italy with a stay at Padua in the winter of 1599–1600 where he attended lectures by Galileo; a shorter visit was made during the summer of 1601. The antiquities of Venice, Florence, Siena and Rome attracted him as did erupting Vesuvius and the Swiss mountains which he saw when he returned to France. Ever a travel-

*TAYLOR, p. 196.

ler, he then journeyed to Paris to view the shrines of the ancient kings, then on to London where he was received by King James. He returned via the Low Countries with stops at centers of learning in Leyden, Amsterdam and the main cities of Belgium.

Peiresc returned to France in 1607 and put on display in his Chateau de Beaugencier the books, manuscripts, paintings, medals and scientific instruments that he had acquired in his travels and by later purchase. He visited the important libraries, and savants from all Europe came to view the works in Greek, Hebrew, Syriac and Coptic that he placed before them. Among those who shared his hospitality was Cardinal Barberini and thru Cardinal Bagni he sent a score of Greek manuscript volumes of commentaries on Plato and Aristotle to Rome. He was equally generous with scholars in other cities in Europe, returning any kindness shown him many fold. His home became an academy of the learned and he served as Senator in the Parliament at Aix.

He died on 24 June 1637 aged 57 and was buried in the Dominican Church at Aix. At a commemorative session called by the Academy in Rome to honor his memory ten Cardinals attended and the eulogies filled a thick volume. Such was the man to whom Galileo turned to share his concern about matters of priority and pressure. He wrote to Peiresc on 22 February 1635, "I do not hope for any relief, and that is because I have committed no crime. I might hope for and obtain pardon, if I had erred; for it is to faults that the prince can bring indulgence, whereas against one wrongfully sentenced while he was innocent, it is expedient, in order to put up a show of strict lawfulness, to uphold rigor . . . But my most holy intention, how clearly would it appear if some

NICOLAVS, FABRICIVS, DE, PEIRESE,

Claude de Peiresc

The correspondent of Galileo, learned, wealthy and helpful to him in his
post-trial troubles. An ardent astronomer, he fostered learning from his
home in Aix-en-Provence.

power would bring to light the slanders, frauds, stratagems, and trickeries that were used eighteen years ago in Rome in order to deceive the authorities! . . ." On 16 March he wrote, "You have read my writings, and from them you have certainly understood which was the true and real motive that caused, under the lying mask of religion, this war against me that continually restrains and undercuts me in all directions, so that neither can help come to me from outside nor can I go forth to defend myself, there having been issued an express order to all Inquisitors that they should not allow any of my works to be reprinted which had been printed many years ago or grant permission to any new work that I would print."*

From the biography of Peiresc published by Pierre Gassendi in 1651 and translated into English by William Rand in 1657 we gather the details of this unusually rich and generous life during the formative years of science. His vast correspondence with the savants of Europe came to 10,000 letters (which his niece destroyed following his death). From this book we learn of Peiresc's deep feeling for Galileo as a teacher in mathematics after they met at the home of Pinelli.

News of the use by Galileo of the telescope reached Peiresc in February 1610 and efforts were made to obtain a copy of the *Siderius Nuncius*. This was finally done but an actual telescope was much more difficult to get; yet by November the satellites of Jupiter were observed, to the great joy of Peiresc. Telescopes were then ordered from Italy, Holland and Paris and an observatory was instituted. Before long 40 telescopes of

varying quality were gathered there. Correspondence with Kepler carried astronomical data and Peiresc proposed naming the four satellites of Jupiter after four members of the Medici family—for two princes and two princesses.

The arrival of Galileo's *Two Systems* sent Peiresc into another series of confirming observations and calculations on the motion of the tides and the diurnal and annual motion of the earth. The appearance of the book with ecclesiastic approval seemed to Peiresc as pointing to a new day in the freedom of pursuing scientific truth. The references to the lodestone and the work of Gilbert in England were further signs of this extension of thought. Peiresc requested of Galileo a telescope of the clearest lenses and best resolution so that Peiresc could himself make better observations. Then, in 1635, Gassendi reported that Peiresc had ". . . first writ many letters, by which he thought he might be allowed to comfort such a friend, and to condole with him for his hard hap. Moreover about this time, he took a great deal of care, endeavouring by means of the most excellent Cardinal, that the Sentence of *Galileus* might be moderated, and he restored to his liberty; Which he did of his own accord, judging that the duty of a friend required as much of him, and the merits of that man, whose memory would be delightful to Posterity." Later he added, ". . . giving himself up in his latter years, to the study of Astronomy, so as to build a most high Tower, furnished with plenty of Instruments belonging to that Art, where he watched all night long, when the Skie was clear, in Contemplation of the Starres: not only diligently observing their Altitudes, Magnitudes and Motions; but penetrating by the quickness of his wit, into

---

* de SANTILLANA, *Crime of Galileo*, p. 324.

their very matter and Nature; assisted by that new and admirable Invention of the Telescope, which makes the most remote and obscure Species and Representations of things, clearly to be seen, whose name and use was invented by *Galileus*, the Prince doubtless of Mathematicians, and a very loving friend of our *Peireskius*. By the help of which Instrument *Peireskius* caused the several faces and appearances, both of the other Planets, and also of the Moon, with the smallest marks and spots as it were, which appeared therein, to be diligently viewed and engraven in Copper Plates:

committing to writing, his own perpetual observations thereof; so that no man was better acquainted with this World of ours, than *Peireskius* was with the Heavenly Orbs; especially the Moon, which the ancient Sages of Italy were wont to call Antichthon, the other Earth. Whole Eclipses he did both observe himself, and caused them, by all Mathematicians, to be more diligently observed than formerly. . . ."*

------
*GASSENDUS, Petrus, *The Mirrour of True Nobility & Gentility. Being the Life of the Renowned Nicolaus Claudius Fabricius Lord of Peiresk*, London, 1657, Book V, pp. 134, 263.

Ex Museo Pisanorum

GALILEO GALILEI

Ottavio Leoni painted Galileo's portrait in 1624 but this has vanished. There remains a sketch in crayon and this engraving made by the artist at the time of Galileo's visit to Rome to plead with the newly chosen Pope Urban VIII to liberalize the church position on the Copernican doctrine.

A LONG-LOST LETTER of GALILEO
to PEIRESC on a MAGNETIC CLOCK

by Stillman Drake[*]

DURING a visit to England in July, 1961, I was privileged to meet Mr. Kenneth K. Knight and to see his distinguished collection of early scientific books, instruments, and manuscripts. Among these was an autograph letter of Galileo which Mr. Knight graciously permitted me to publish. The letter, in an excellent state of preservation, is written on the first two sides of a single folded sheet measuring 40 cm x 27.7 cm when opened. On its face, in the upper left-hand margin, is the single word, "Galilei," in an early script; with this exception, the entire document is in Galileo's own writing. The letter is without direction or cover sheet, but is easily identifiable as a reply transmitted to Peiresc with the aid of Roberto Galilei at Lyons.[1] Contemporary references to this reply mentioned it by date, but it had long been presumed lost.[2]

The correspondence of which this letter forms an essential part began on 26 January 1634, when Peiresc wrote to Galileo recalling his brief residence in Padua "more than thirty years ago," and his presence at some of Galileo's public lectures there.[3] At Gassendi's request, Peiresc sent along to Galileo a letter from Gassendi and a letter and book by Martin Hortensio. Peiresc himself wrote to second the request made in Gassendi's letter for the use of one of Galileo's telescopes, their own instruments being unsatisfactory for observations which they wished to pursue. All these letters and the book were transmitted by Peiresc to G. G. Bouchard at Rome. Bouchard in due course added certain other letters and one of his own, forwarding the lot to Galileo on 18 March.[4]

From Arcetri, on 25 July, Galileo wrote at length to Elia Diodati in Paris. At the same time he sent lenses for a telescope to be forwarded to Gassendi, asking that Peiresc

---

[*] Based on one of a series of studies appearing in ISIS under the general title GALILEO GLEANINGS of which this was No. XII. This is now republished with changes with the kind permission of the editors of ISIS. Mr. Drake resides in San Francisco, California. The Galileo letter to Peiresc is now in the Burndy Library.

[1] Roberto was a distant relative of Galileo's, about thirty years his junior, who served as intermediary for much of Galileo's foreign correspondence after the trial of 1633. His brother Girolamo resided in Florence. By the use of these family connections, Galileo probably managed to escape rigorous censorship.

[2] The letter was received by Peiresc on 25 May (Opere XVI, 268.) Its supposed loss was noted as recently as 1959 by Cornelis de Waard in the Correspondance du P. Marin Mersenne, V, 243, n. 3 and 222, n. 1.

[3] Peiresc had dwelt twice at Padua during his student days, first in the winter of 1599–1600, and again very briefly in the summer of 1601.

[4] Opere XVI, 64. By coincidence, Bouchard's letter also announced to Galileo the arrival at Rome of the German Jesuit Father Athanasius Kircher with a mysterious clock which is further discussed below.

The water-clock of Father Linus as depicted in Pietrasancta's *De Symbolis Heroicis*, 1634.

the restrictions imposed upon Galileo.[6] At the same time he wrote directly to Peiresc, mentioning the letter of Galileo that he had sent to Gassendi.[7]

Peiresc, who had previously obtained a copy of the sentence pronounced against Galileo, wrote early in December to Cardinal Barberini, remonstrating in the strongest terms against the treatment of his former friend and teacher. Among other things, he said that it would be a blemish upon the reputation of Pope Urban VIII (uncle to the cardinal) if he should fail to give Galileo his special protection and some particular assistance.[8] This courageous appeal, however, elicited from the cardinal only the rather cool response: "I shall not fail to convey to His Holiness what you write me about Galileo; but as I am one, albeit the least, of the cardinals who attend meetings of the Holy Office, you will excuse me if I do not extend myself to reply to you in more detail."[9]

Early in February 1635, Roberto Galilei obtained and forwarded to Galileo copies both of Peiresc's plea and the cardinal's reply.[10] Galileo promptly wrote to thank Peiresc in an eloquent letter, remarking that he expected no relief, precisely because he had committed no crime, whereas clemency derives from forgiveness and not from admission of juridical error.[11] Meanwhile the dauntless Peiresc had already replied to the cardinal, predicting that posterity would regard the persecution of Galileo just as men

also be allowed to use them, and apologizing for his not having replied directly to Peiresc in view of a host of troubles that forced him to abstain from all but the most necessary activities.[5] The package containing the lenses was in fact long delayed in transit, and did not reach Diodati until about the beginning of November. On the tenth of that month he sent them on to Gassendi with a copy of Galileo's letter, and suggested that Peiresc might use his good offices with the powerful Francesco Cardinal Barberini to obtain some moderation of

[5] *Ibid.*, 115–119.

[6] *Ibid.*, 153.

[7] *Ibid.*, 154. A copy of Galileo's letter, probably that which was sent to Gassendi, was forwarded to Peiresc; a notation in his hand appears on the copy published by Favaro, the original being lost.

[8] *Ibid.*, 169–171.

[9] *Ibid.*, 187 (2 January 1635).

[10] *Ibid.*, 206–207 (7 February).

[11] *Ibid.*, 215–216 (21 or 22 February).

looked upon that of Socrates.[12] Somehow a copy of this letter also reached Galileo, and he wrote again to Peiresc (16 March) in admiration of his persistence in beating against a rock that gave no sign of yielding to any blows, even to those so well aimed.[13] To Galileo's first letter, Peiresc had replied at great length on the first of April. After giving reasons for his persistence and outlining his future strategy, he wrote as follows:

"But to keep the matter alive, His Eminence having written me that Father Sylvester Pietrasancta had presented to him a book of his, *De symbolis heroicis*,[14] which the Father had shown me here when passing through at Christmas with Monsignor [Pierluigi] Caraffa, Nuncio of Cologne, I took occasion to remind His Eminence that if the press of other and more worthy affairs had not permitted him to read or scan that book, he might deign to read in Book IV, Chapter V, what the author says about a water-clock devised by Father Linus,[15] of which you will see here the diagram and description, which is a marvelous thing, if indeed it works; and since the author of the book says nothing of having seen the machine itself, nor does he name anyone who has seen it, I begged His Eminence to call in

Father Sylvester and ask him as to the real truth of this machine and to get also the opinion of Msgr. Caraffa, who ought to know about it, not only from having seen something of it, but perhaps also by having penetrated its secret. And I also wrote, under the same cover, not only to Father Sylvester, who is now at the Collegio Romano, but to the said Nuncio (who, passing through here incognito, had wished to spend a couple of hours in my study with Father Sylvester), telling them both of my regret, after they had left, that I had forgotten to speak with them about that machine of Father Linus, in order to learn from them directly what could be believed of it; and thus they are under obligation not only to give an account of this to His Eminence, but also to give me some share and part in their dealings with him. Whence I hope at the proper time to take occasion to reopen your Excellency's case with greater vigor and effectiveness than before, inasmuch as if the machine truly works (as Peter Paul Rubens writes me from Anversa in a letter of 16 March, which I received yesterday afternoon, he having heard the testimony of Father Sylvester and others who affirm it to be as represented, Father Sylvester having added to him that he had seen it at his leisure, and that Msgr. Caraffa had taken it to his house to examine it at his ease, and having observed it for some days, found it to be most exact), it seems that this is a proof and testimony fallen from heaven into the hands of a Jesuit Father rather than anyone of another profession, to leave no suspicion against the testimony of the father who invented it and that other who published it, in order to overthrow the error of those who find so much repugnance in the Copernican doctrine and in what you have

---

[12] *Ibid.*, 202.

[13] *Ibid.*, 215–216.

[14] Antwerp, 1634. The frontispiece of this book was designed by Rubens, which explains the fact that Peiresc turned to him, among others, for light on this device. A copy of the relevant diagram and passage from the book was found among Peiresc's papers, and one was probably sent to Galileo with this letter.

[15] Francis Linus (*vere* Hall) was born at London in 1595 and entered the Society of Jesus in 1623. He taught mathematics at Liège for 22 years, after which he resided principally in England. Linus is remembered principally for his criticisms of Robert Boyle, which stimulated the latter to publish a precise formulation of his gas law.

proposed in sport and as a puzzle. Signor Rubens, a great admirer of your genius, even promised me to ride post to Liège to visit Father Linus and see his machine, which he will not do without giving me an account of it; and I have urged him to do so as soon as possible; and I shall seek some dealings and correspondence with Father Linus through Msgr. Caraffa and Father Sylvester or others, since they knew him; rather, I shall seek to have him called to Rome, and arrange that he take the road through these countries, to enjoy his passage and draw from him the most I can by word of mouth, if he does not bring with him the water-clock so that we can see it here in his hands; and all this is to have always new devices to remind those of you who can aid you better than I can." [16]

II.

Here we may well pause to consider the reasons for Peiresc's great excitement over this reported device, which he evidently believed to be of such importance that it might convince even the authorities at Rome of the earth's diurnal rotation, and thus induce them to relax the sentence against Galileo and the ban on the Copernican theory. A summary of the state of affairs at that time has already been written by Cornelis de Waard in a note on a letter sent by Godfrey Wendelin to Mersenne in 1633, which we cannot do better than to quote, particularly as it contains the very passage from Pietrasancta's book alluded to by Peiresc:

" Projects for such magnetic clocks may be traced back to Roger Bacon and Peter de Marincourt, whose booklet was in print after 1588. Cardan and Jean Taisnier also made mention of these supposed perpetual motions. Gilbert had assumed, to explain the diurnal motion of the earth, that a suspended magnetic sphere could set itself in rotation, but this opinion was refuted by Galileo in his work of 1632. Among the first scholars who had knowledge of Father Linus's magnetic clock we find the nuncio Caraffa and his Jesuit confessor, Father Sylvester Pietrasancta. The former had taken the clock to his house, and after observing it for a day or two found it accurate. The latter gave the ensuing picture and description of it in a book published in 1634, though the licenses were dated the previous year:

I know the effects of the magnetic stone are utterly remarkable, and from its power something new is always being produced. Thus at Liège recently, in the English College of our Society, Father Franciscus Linus, teacher of mathematics, invented a most pleasing globe, which placed at the center of surrounding fluid in a vessel (as the earth is surrounded with air) preserves a mysterious balancing of its mass. But the rotation of the heavens from east to west nevertheless, by an occult force and as if it were lovingly followed, drives it completely about in the space of twenty-four hours. A little fish is placed inside as indicator, and like an expert swimmer, its weight poised, watches the fleeting hours and designates them with its snout, its eyes gazing intently on them. If by motion of the vessel the water takes away the impetus, the globe soon regains its course by its own accord, and the ratio of the time is thoroughly consistent after tranquillity is restored. Also the indicator

---

[16] *Opere* XVI, 245 ff.

placed in the vessel in like manner shows the hours. And it imitates the sun in his sphere, and indeed follows the sun in the east, on the meridian, in the west; and what is more, from the seat of its driving out, at that place it requires and seeks again agreement with the stations of the stars. So much the more will it be hastened, because love does not know delay; nevertheless, while it leaps ahead sometimes and springs back, at length it gets to a place in which it again unerringly accompanies the sun. . . .

" Perhaps Mersenne, influenced by theories that attributed a magnetic action to the sun which moved the planets, saw in this (as Peiresc did later) an argument for the Copernican hypothesis. But the water-clock of Father Linus, which did not turn consistently during twenty-four hours, has nothing to do with the diurnal movement of the earth; moreover, when one compares it with the apparatus of the same kind set up by Father Kircher, its operation seems evident." [17]

Two kinds of odd "clocks" had made their appearance about this time, one kind purporting to be governed by magnetic force, and the other to be influenced by the occult properties of seeds or roots of plants which tend to face the sun. One of the latter, exhibited by Kircher, had been mentioned by Bouchard to Galileo in a letter previously cited, and was more fully described to him in a letter from Rafael Magiotti written on the same day:

" There is now at Rome a Jesuit, long in the Orient, who, besides knowing twelve languages and being a good mathematician

etc., has with him many lovely things, among them a root which turns as the sun turns, and serves as a most perfect clock. This is affixed by him in a piece of cork, which holds it freely on the water, and on this cork there is a needle of iron that shows the hours, with a scale for knowing what hour it is in other parts of the world. He has two roots which attract each other as a magnet attracts iron." [18]

The story of Kircher's "botanical clock," Linus's magnetic clock, and Kircher's later plagiarism of the latter device, was given at length by Georges Monchamps.[19] That there was some kind of device similar to that described by Magiotti can hardly be doubted, as Kircher exhibited it to many persons at Aix, Avignon, and Rome, after obtaining a supply of the mysterious root from an Arab merchant at Marseilles in 1633. Monchamps appears to have accepted the belief of Kircher's contemporaries that it was sunflower root or seed, with an innate property of following the sun (even at night!). Possibly it was some aromatic root, and in any case it probably acted (as will chips of camphor) by affecting the surface tension of the water in a restricted area. The cork may be presumed to have been fairly large and flat, and to have been prevented from moving laterally by some sort of pivot or by a rod inserted through a central hole.

Linus's clock was a very different matter. He did not divulge its secret, but Kircher was able to divine this, and published it as his own in the *Magnes*. The reconstruction

---

[17] De Waard, *op. cit.*, III, 435–436.

[18] *Opere* XVI, 65. Probably the attraction of the two roots was also observed on the surface of water, and was similarly a surface-tension phenomenon, as explained below.

[19] *Galilée et la Belgique* (Saint-Troud. 1892), pp. 127–141.

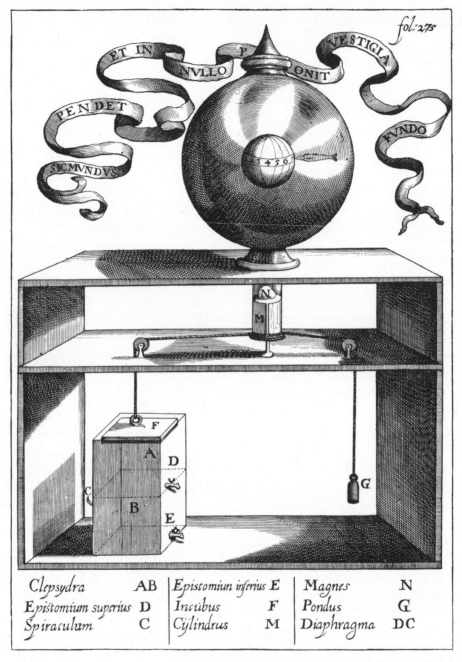

Clepsydra	AB	Epistomiun inferius	E	Magnes	N
Epistomium superius	D	Incubus	F	Pondus	G
Spiraculum	C	Cylindrus	M	Diaphragma	DC

Kircher, *Magnes*, 1643

Following the design shown by Pietrasancta in 1634 the Jesuit scientist
Athanasius Kircher included a similar design in his book on the magnet
that first appeared in 1641. The engraving shows the driving clepsydral
mechanism for actuating the magnet N; drapes hid the mechanism from
view.

by Monchamps assumes the globe to have been suspended by a fine silk thread, invisible to the naked eye, which he deduces from the experimental difficulty of maintaining exact equilibrium, and from Pietrasancta's observation that when disturbed, the globe overshot the mark somewhat in returning to its original course, a phenomenon attributed by Monchamps to torsion of a thread. To account for the rotation of the suspended globe, Monchamps assumes that a bit of iron, attached to the inside of the globe, was acted upon by a magnet hidden in the hollow wooden base and driven by some sort of clockwork, possibly clepsydral. A very similar account, he says, is given by Kircher. He notes, however, that in an earlier section of the *Magnes*, Kircher had described a different method of suspending a solid mass in a fluid; namely, by utilizing two layers of fluid similar in color but differing in density.[20]

The explanations offered by Kircher, Monchamps, and (as we shall see) by Galileo appear to be correct in principle but to require some refinement. The suggestion of a thread-suspension to account for certain observed oscillations of the globe is liable to the objection that a thread sufficiently strong to produce them would quickly be-

come wound to a tension capable of checking the progress of the globe. Moreover, it would be difficult to secure the two ends of the thread in a glass sphere without permitting leakage of the fluid. Equilibrium must therefore have been maintained by the use of two fluids; but then, if a piece of iron or lodestone were affixed near the perimeter of the wax globe, it would always tend to approach the concealed attracting magnet, thus preventing any effective horizontal rotation.

In all probability, the hollow wax globe was pierced horizontally by a compass needle or its equivalent, and the concealed mechanism simply rotated a bar magnet or elongated piece of lodestone centered beneath it. Such a system assures horizontal stability of the globe. Assuming the magnet to move jerkily, this device would exhibit periodically a notable oscillation of its own when one end of the needle approached and passed the earth's magnetic pole. If this happened to occur about the time of sunset and sunrise, it would produce the curious effect which contemporary observers attributed to an exchange of solar for stellar influence.[21]

III.

To return to Peiresc's long letter of 1 April 1635: this was duly sent to Roberto Galilei, who forwarded it to Galileo on 16 April. The next day, Peiresc received Galileo's second letter of thanks (dated 16 March), and immediately wrote again at considerable length, referring several times to the device displayed by Linus, as well as

---

[20] This suggestion, as will be seen, brings Kircher's explanation into complete conformity with that of Galileo. It is not impossible that word of the contents of Galileo's letter to Peiresc had reached Kircher before 1641, when the first edition of the *Magnes* was published. Nor is it entirely beyond belief that Galileo had described (or even built) such a device many years earlier, as he says, in which case both Linus and Kircher may have heard accounts of it during the period of widespread intense interest in the lodestone and its properties. On the whole, however, it appears most likely that Galileo and Kircher each independently deduced the nature of the mechanism that must have been employed by Linus, and that the English Jesuit was the only one actually to have built a model.

[21] For some of the suggestions in this reconstruction, as well as for the interpretation of Pietrasancta's florid prose, I am indebted to conversations with my son Daniel.

to the (thermometric) circular tubes containing liquid which had been constructed by Cornelius Drebbel as a tidal model. Thence he went on to observations of his own about tides, and to tentative conjectures about the mechanism of the water-clock and its value in proof of the Copernican system.[22] Peiresc had in fact already become so confident of securing amelioration of Galileo's sentence that he took steps to delay publication by Diodati of Bernegger's Latin translation of the *Dialogo* lest this damage his chances of success.[23]

To all this good-hearted but mistaken enthusiasm, Galileo responded in the following words, translated from the original letter here reproduced in facsimile.

Most distinguished and excellent Sir, my esteemed patron:

Your Excellency's letter, filled throughout with feelings of courtesy and goodwill, continues to make the fortune of my misfortune appear sweeter to me, and in a certain way to bless the persecutions of my enemies, without which there would have remained concealed from me that which is most to be admired in humanity, and the benign inclination of many of my noble patrons, and above all your Excellency's love; all which, since it does not deserve to be aroused by any worthy talent that Nature might have reposed in me, Fortune has instead made up for through you by kindling in their minds the fire of charity, by which they are moved to compassion for my situation, in which, in addition to the reason mentioned, there is for me no little comfort in believing that it is not a spirit of ever-increasing cruelty that continues to hold me under oppression,[24] but rather, as I shall say, a sort of official policy on the part of those who want to cover up the original error of having wronged an innocent man, by continuing their offenses and wrongs so that people will conceive that other grave demerits, not made public, may exist to aggravate the guilt of the culprit. Well, let it be as pleases him to whom is granted the power to do what he will; for in all events I shall remain perpetually obliged to the consummate goodness of your Excellency, who is so energetically aroused in my interest, and with such industry and vigilance goes dauntlessly thinking up means to be of assistance to me.

The water-clock will truly be a thing of extreme marvel if it is true that the globe suspended in the middle of the water goes naturally turning by an occult magnetic force. Many years ago I made a similar invention, but with the aid of a deceptive artifice, and the machine was this. The little globe with 12 meridians for the 24 hours was of copper, hollow within, with a little piece of magnet placed at the bottom, and almost in balance with the density of water; so that placing in the vessel some salt water,

---

[22] *Opere* XVI, 259–262.
[23] *Ibid.*, 249.

[24] This view had been previously expressed by Galileo in his letter to Diodati; cf. *Opere* XVI, 116, lines 44–45.

Ill.mo et Ecc.mo Sig:re e P.ron mio Col.mo

La lra di V.S. Ill.ma et Ecc.ma sparsa tutta d'affetti di cortesia, e benignità, continua di farmi parer sempre più soave la fortuna del mio infortunio, et in certo modo benedir le persecuzioni de' miei nimici; senza le quali mi sarebbe sempre restata occulta la parte più da stimarsi dell'humanità, e benigna propensione di molti miei sig.ri e P.ron e sopra tutti l'Amore di V.E: il quale nõ meritando d'esser promosso da talento alcuno di virtù che la Natura habbia riposto in me, ha in vece di lei supplito la sorte cõ accender nelle lor menti il fuoco della carità, cõ la quale vanno compatessionando lo stato mio; nel quale oltre alla ragion detta mi è di nõ piccolo sollevam.to il creder che, non un'animo che sempre più si vada inasprendo sia quello che continui di tenermi oppresso, ma più presto una quasi dirò ragion di stato di quelli che voglion ricoprir il primo errore d'haver altro reo offeso un'innocẽ ti, col continuar l'offese, e i torti, acciò l'universale si formi cõcetto possano altri gravi demeriti nõ fatti palesi aggravarla la colpa del reo. Hor sia quel che piace à chi è conceduta la potestà di fare il suo arbitrio, che in tutti gl'eventi resterò io spietuam obligato allo cõma bõtà di V.E la quale con tanta premura s'appassiona nel mio interesse, e cõ tanta industria, e vigilanza indefessam va spiestando i mezzi che possano essermi di sollevam.to.

L'Horologio hydraulico sarà veram cosa di estrema maraviglia, quando sia vero che il Globo pendente nel mezzo dell'Acqua vadia naturalm volgendosi p occulta virtù magnetica. Io feci già molti anni sono una simile inventione; ma cõ l'aiuto d'un'inganno e l'artifizio, e la machina era tale. Il Globetto diviso cõ 12 meridiani p le 24 hore era di rame, voto dentro, e cõ un pezzetto di calamita, postogli nel fondo, equilibrato quasi alla gravità dell'acqua, siche posta nel vaso una parte d'acqua salata, e poi sopra quella altra dolce, il Globo si fermava tra le due acque, cioè nel mezzo del vaso: il qual vaso posava sopra un piede di legno dentro al quale stava ascoso un horologio fabbricato à posta con tal'arte che girava un pezzo di calamita, che sopra vi era accomodata, facendogli fare una revolutione i 24 hore al cui moto ubidiva l'altra calamita posta nel globetto facendolo girare, e mostrar le hore. Sin qui arrivò già la mia speculatione: ma se questa del P. Lino senz'altro artifizio fa sì il suo Globo ubidisca al moto del Cielo, sarà veram cosa celeste, e divina, et haremo un Moto spetuo.

V.E con quei mezzi che va nominando potrà facilm venire in cognizione del tutto, io tra tan to nell'hò voluto significare il mio pensiero p havere un testimonio omai exceptione maius che nõ hò usurpata l'inventione al P. Lino; se però la sua machina nõ havesse altro di più che la mia.

Non devo nascondere à V.E come sentendo un Principe girate l'ordine mandato dal S.to Off.o à tutti gl'Inquisitori di nõ dar licenza nõ solam che si ristampi alcuna delle opere mie già molti anni fà pubblicate, ma che nõ si licenzj alcuna di nuove chè io, ed altri volesse stampare, à che la proibizione è de omnibz editis, et edendis, e preso assunto di fare stampare il resto delle mie fatiche nõ publicate ancora, o forse vi è mosso p curiosità di veder l'esito di questa impresa, e che fortuna correranno tali materie lontaniss: da propoziz attenenti à religioni più che nõ è il Cielo dalla Terra. Io cõtro à mia voglia sono stato forzato à concederne copia à S.A. sicuro ch'à me nõ ne possa succeder se nõ qualche travaglio; se bene nõ mi è stata fatta, ne accennata proibizione alcuna, p so che nõ devo ne anco haver notizia del divieto fatto à gl'Inquisitori; p lo che questo ch'esseriso à V.E. sia detto in cõfidenza. Da questo, e dall'esser state raccolte in Firenze, et in Roma tutte l'opere mie, sì che più nõ se ne trovano p le librerie, ass tam ci scorge che si fa ogni opera p levar dal mõdo la mia memoria; nella qual vanità, se cõpessero i mi avversarij quanto poco io premo, forse nõ si mostrerebbero tanto ansiosi d'opprimermi.

Io nõ finirò di parlar cõ lei senza di nuovo ringraziarla della sua infinita benignità, e del fervor col quale invigila ne miei interessi, e se il sollevare chi p fior di tutti sue colpe viene travagliato è atto meritorio, può V.E. viver sicura che ne ricevera guiderdone dalla divina bonità. E qui cõ reverte affetto gli bacio le mani, e nella sua buona graa mi raccom̃do

Dalla Villa d'Arcetri li 12 di Maggio 1635

Di V.S. Ill̃ma et Ecc̃ma

Devõ: Et Obblig: Ser:

Galileo Galilej

and then on that some sweet water, the globe stayed between the two waters, that is, in the middle of the vessel, which vessel had a wooden base in which there was concealed a clock made expressly in such a way as to rotate a piece of magnet that was fitted upon it, making one revolution in 24 hours, which motion the other magnet placed in the little globe obeyed, making it turn and show the hour. Thus far went my speculation; but if this one of Father Linus without any trickery makes his globe obey the motion of the heavens, truly it will be a celestial and divine thing, and we shall have a perpetual motion. Your Excellency, by those means which you recite, will easily be able to come to a knowledge of the whole matter; I, meanwhile, have wished to indicate my thought in order to have a witness beyond all exception that I have not usurped the invention from Father Linus—if indeed his machine does not have any more to it than mine.

I should not hide from your Excellency that a great prince, hearing of the order sent by the Holy Office to all the Inquisitors not to license not only the reprinting of any work of mine published many years ago, but not to license anything new that I and others wish to publish, so that the prohibition is *de omnibus editis et edendis*, has undertaken the task of having the balance of my still unpublished labors printed, and perhaps he has been moved by curiosity to see the outcome of this undertaking, and the fortune encountered by such materials,

more remote from propositions pertaining to religion than are the heavens from the earth. I, against my will, was constrained to grant a copy to his Highness, certain that for my part only some travail must ensue, though I had not been given any prohibition whatever, nor the hint of one, since I might not even be notified of the ban given to the Inquisitors; wherefore let this that I impart to your Excellency be said in confidence. From this, and from the fact that in Florence and in Rome all my works have been called in, so that no more are to be found in the bookstores, it is easy to see that every effort is being made to remove all memory of me from the world, but if my adversaries knew how little I strive for such a vanity, perhaps they would not show themselves so anxious to oppress me.

I cannot conclude speaking to you without again thanking you for your infinite kindness, and for the fervor with which you keep watch over my interests; and if it is a meritorious act to comfort one who is in trouble through no faults of his own, your Excellency may live in certainty of receiving reward from divine Providence. And here with reverent affection I kiss your hands, and in your good grace I am rejoiced.

From the Villa of Arcetri, the 12th of May, 1635

from your Illustrious and Excellent Lordship's

Most devoted and obligated servitor,

Galileo Galilei

The letter was sent to Peiresc in care of Roberto Galilei, who on 28 May wrote to say:

" I have read and reread many times the letter your Excellency has written to the distinguished Councillor of Peiresc. Truly it is a golden letter, not only for the polish of its style, but for your Excellency's having exposed the stratagem of Father Linus, which I do not believe to be other than that which you describe in this letter. I sent your letter immediately to the said gentleman, and for my part I hope you shall have an answer to it. . . . Shortly after writing yours of the 12th, you will have received the others, as I have a letter of that date from my brother Girolamo saying that he had them ready to deliver to you." [25]

Peiresc received Galileo's letter on 25 May, and wrote to Gassendi the next day that "if my man had transcribed the letter, as I instructed him to, you should now see the copy, for I am sending the original unsealed to Mons. Rossi[26] and [thence] to Mons. Diodati tomorrow, God willing. . . ." [27]

It appears that God was willing, but the secretary was weak, and thus the letter passed from Peiresc's hands without a copy having been preserved among his papers, or Gassendi's. The original probably found its way safely to Diodati, but has wandered ever since without finding its way into the published correspondence either of its celebrated writer or its distinguished recipient.

It may be noted that Peiresc put off answering Galileo's letter because of an expected visit of Henry Dormalius, who on his behalf had carefully observed the device of Father Linus. When he finally made his report (about 18 June), Peiresc found the evidence unsatisfactory, and concluded that some artifice similar to that described by Galileo must have been employed by the Jesuit, as he then wrote to Gassendi. [28]

The only other known letter from Peiresc to Galileo is dated 24 February 1637, shortly before the death of Peiresc. In it he recounted the fortunes of his various pleas to Cardinal Barberini on Galileo's behalf, and described some observations that had been made with the excellent lenses sent by Galileo to Gassendi; but he did not again refer to the affair of the magnetic water-clock. [29]

[25] Ibid., 269.
[26] Sieur de Rossy, superintendent of posts at Lyons.
[27] Opere XVI, 268.
[28] Ibid., 280.
[29] Opere XVII, 33.

The coat of arms of Galileo
Galilei as painted on the walls
of the University of Padua
where he taught from 1592 to
1610.